A SOUL'S JOURNEY

Peter Richelieu

*To Kim with love
from Debby –
June 1996 –

Keep up the search!*

Thorsons
An Imprint of HarperCollinsPublishers

Dedicated to
All Those Who Seek

Thorsons
An Imprint of HarperCollins*Publishers*
77–85 Fulham Palace Road,
Hammersmith, London W6 8JB
1160 Battery Street,
San Francisco, California 94111–1213

First published in South Africa as *From the Turret*
by Graphic Stationers and Publishers, Durban
Published by The Aquarian Press 1989
This edition published by Thorsons 1996

1   3   5   7   9   10   8   6   4   2

A catalogue record for this book
is available from the British Library

ISBN 0 7225 3291 1

Typeset by Harper Phototypesetters Limited
Northampton, England
Printed in Great Britain by
HarperCollinsManufacturing Glasgow

'As a man casts off old clothes and puts on new ones, so the embodied self, casting off old bodies proceeds to other and new ones'

Bhagavad Gita

PREFACE

In spite of the fact that I am no writer and claim no gifts or experience in that direction, this book is given to the world without apology, for I am carrying out orders from those who must be obeyed.

The part of the book which will hold the interest of the largest number of readers is that which begins at Chapter Four. For those people who have no recollection of their life and activities during sleep, even this part will contain many completely new ideas. As many of these call for explanation, readers are advised to avoid the temptation of skimming quickly through the preliminary chapters in order to reach this one more quickly! These introductory chapters, which are written in the form of talks by a Hindu guru, are so filled with vital information that they hold the key not only to what follows in the book but to what happens to all of us at one time or another. Those who read them slowly and carefully and who refer to them often, will glean the most general information and acquire the best groundwork for the appreciation of the story which follows.

In writing down my experiences I have added no embellishments. If these experiences help a few of you to understand the scheme of life and so be comforted, if they give you an insight into the nature of evolution and provide you with a reason for making friends of animals – they will not have been written in vain.

PETER RICHELIEU

PROLOGUE

≈

It was the 7th of July 1941, and I was still brooding over a cable I had received from the War Office in London three days before, telling me that Charles, my dear young brother, had been killed in action over England. He was only twenty-three; more than a year before he had joined the RAF and qualified as a pilot. Of course we were proud of him – who would not want to join the RAF, if he were twenty-one years of age, fit as a fiddle and eager to do his bit for the old country? Naturally we knew that the life of a pilot was precarious, but somehow it did not seem that anything could happen to him. People are often like that with those they love, and Charles and I had always been closer to each other than ordinary brothers although there was a difference of ten years in our ages.

I remembered the first time he proudly told us he had downed his first enemy plane. The initial shock from the news of Charles' death was severe, and now, for the first time in my life, I felt bitter against the Powers that Be, the beneficent Creator who is talked of so glibly. How could He be beneficent if He allowed the innocent to be killed?

I had been brought up a Catholic, not a very strict one perhaps, and I had taken many things for granted, in the way Christians do. Religion was part of one's life and, on certain days, time had to be given to it; at other times one did not think very much about what was expected of a Christian, a follower of Christ. Now I thought about these things for the first time, and I did not feel that I wanted to go to church – certainly not to a priest. I did not want to pray; why should I? God had taken away from me the dearest thing I possessed in the world, and although I did not curse God, I certainly came very near to hating Him. A friend had told me that Charles was well out of this war, that the next world was most certainly a better place than this one at the moment, and that I should be thankful. But I was not thankful; I had so much looked forward to see his cheery face and hear his hearty laugh at his next leave – which we had arranged to spend together. Now the future was a blank.

It was in just this mood that I sat on the never-to-be-forgotten morning a few weeks ago – the day *he* came. Although now, judging from the change which has taken place in me, it seems as if it could all have taken place in a former existence, yet I can remember every detail, and shall until I die. I shall try to tell the story just as it happened, but if the recording seems to be disjointed you must forgive me, for I have never tried to write a story before and only do so now because I want others to be comforted, even as I was comforted.

About 11 o'clock on that morning there was a knock at the door, and my servant told me that there was a man in the hall who wished to see me. 'What sort of man?' I asked. His reply was: 'A strange man, master, I think perhaps he come to beg.' I told the boy to go down and enquire what this man wanted and to come back to let me know. On his return he said that the man had a message which could only be given to me, so with some irritation I told him to bring the man up.

Even though I have seen this man very often since then, I still find it difficult to describe him – but I shall do my best. He was tall, slim, about forty-five years of age and wore a beard. He was unmistakably a native of Northern India, though his skin was almost as white as mine. He was dressed in a simple Indian costume made of material so indiscriminate in colour that at first sight one might have thought it was dirty, but on closer inspection one saw that it was spotlessly clean. His feet were encased in sandals and he wore a turban.

I told the boy to go, and asked my visitor to sit down. He sat down, not on the chair that I had indicated but cross-legged on the carpet.

It was then that I noticed the benevolent expression of his eyes, which seemed to contain the wisdom of the ages. So far he had not spoken.

'Well,' I said, 'what can I do for you?'

He seemed surprised at the question, and took a few seconds to answer it. '*You sent for me*,' he said.

This was too much for me, so I replied: 'What on earth do you mean? I've never set eyes on you before, so am I likely to have sent for you? Come on, tell me what you want, for I have work to do.'

'*You sent for me*,' he repeated, and I suppose the surprise I felt must have been evident in my expression, for he smiled and continued: 'Have not you just lost your brother? Is not it true that you have been asking many questions of a hidden Providence, whom you accuse of being instrumental in taking your brother from you? Have not you said many times: 'Why should such things be? Why should he be taken and not others? What is the use of believing in a god, when you cannot ask him questions and get from him the answers to those questions which mean so much to you?' For the last three nights, when you have slept, you have dreamt that you have been talking to your brother. You *have* been talking to him; you have asked these questions and many others during these hours of fitful sleep. I am the answer to these questions. I am the messenger who has been sent to make these things clear to you, for did not Christ say: 'Ask and it shall be given to you; knock and it shall be opened unto you.' You have asked – you have knocked, and it now rests with you whether you still wish to have the answers you have so often clamoured for.'

'Of course I want to hear the answers to my questions,' I said, 'but who are you and how do I know that you can tell me what I want to know? Surely you are a man the same as I, alive and in the flesh, yet you talk of knowing my brother, of talking to him, of hearing me ask the very questions that I have asked. Is this magic, or am I dreaming? Convince me, if you can. You'll find me a good listener, not very credulous I'm afraid, but as you seem to know so much about me already, I'll listen to what you have to say.'

Then he said: 'I am afraid it will take some time to make you understand, but if you are willing to spare the time, I will come to you for an hour or two most days, until my story is concluded. I cannot promise that you will be convinced by all I have to tell you, but I can promise that at least you will be happier than you are now, so for that reason alone, perhaps the time will not entirely be wasted. Is 11 o'clock each morning suitable for you?'

I said: 'Yes, oh yes,' rather wondering what I had let myself in for, but at the same time feeling that I could get rid of him after the first day, if I found there was a catch in the thing.

I looked up to carry on the conversation, but he had gone. There was no one there, although I had not heard the door open or shut. I began to wonder if I had dreamt it all or whether my brain had become a little deranged, owing to worry and lack of sleep. I even sent for my servant and asked him if he really had brought a man up to see me; when he said he had, I asked if he had seen him go, but he said he had not and resolutely denied that anyone could have left my room and gone out by the front door without his seeing him. That did not help and I still wondered if it had been a dream, for somehow the statement of the boy that he had brought the man to me seemed unreal. I decided to wait for the morrow: 11 o'clock was the time he had fixed, and I was certainly going to be in my room at that hour, to see whether he came or not.

Oddly enough I slept that night as I had not slept since I had received that fateful cable; when I woke in the morning, I seemed to have been talking to Charles and telling him about my visitor. In my dreams Charles did not seem to be at all surprised, and I woke with a certainty that my Indian friend would turn up as arranged. I decided I would ask him as soon as he arrived how he managed to go without being seen or heard.

I suppose my door must have been ajar, for just on 11 o'clock a pleasant voice at my elbow said: 'Well, do you still want those questions answered?' I had not heard him come, but in a strange way was so reassured by his presence that I replied: 'Certainly, I am ready.' Without any more casual conversation he sat down on the floor, I leant back in my chair, and he started to tell me the most amazing story I have ever heard – a story that even now I cannot fully understand, but one which rang true from the first word, a story which I feel will ring true for others who may read it.

During all the days which followed, we had little conversation. He came, just as he had done the first day; sometimes he talked for an hour, sometimes longer, and when he had finished for the morning, he put the palms of his hands together in Eastern fashion and went away. I rather think he sensed when I had had enough, when my brain, reeling with strange facts, had reached a stage at which it could take in no more, for I noticed that he sometimes finished suddenly and without a word of farewell left the room, to return the following morning when, without any fresh introduction, he started to speak as if he had just finished the sentence with which his previous day's discourse was completed.

CHAPTER ONE

I have not come to convert you to any new faith, any new philosophy. I have <u>not</u> been sent to you by him who is my Master to provide answers to the questions which puzzle you at present. The only way in which I can do this is to tell you about the fundamental facts of life in the hope that this will give you a foundation of knowledge through which you can build up a philosophy of your own. I shall also assist you in gaining practical experience through which you can prove things for yourself. Much of what I say will sound unusual to you but, in many lives, I have studied much and had proof of which has convinced me that certain facts are true. I have no desire that you accept what I say as facts or truth, for you can only do so when you get to know such things within your own consciousness.

'There is an old saying of the Lord Buddha, Who founded the religion which bears His name, which illustrates my point. One day one of His disciples came to Him and said: 'Lord, whom shall I believe? One man telleth me this and another that, and both seem sure they are right.' The Lord Buddha replied: 'My son, believe not that which any man saith, not even I, the Lord <u>Budd</u>, unless it appeals to your common sense. And even then do not believe it, but treat it as a reasonable hypothesis until such time as you can prove it for yourself.'

'First of all I shall give you a rough outline of the path which is called evolution and of how that indefinable thing called life is found to flow through the kingdoms of Nature.

'Of the source of life, I can give you no idea. I do not know and I have never met anyone who did. But does that matter? All thinking men are agreed that there must be a creative power behind the Universe; whether we think of that Power as a personal God or just the power of creation does not seem to be a matter of great importance. There are many who still like to think of God as a venerable old man with a beard, an idealistic figure based on the highest that each person can imagine, but with unlimited powers and an understanding of justice that is unequalled amongst men. Who shall say that such an idea is foolish? It may satisfy many but it has no foundation in fact, for no man lives who can speak with knowledge of either the creation of the universe or of that thing which we call life.

'Although we cannot analyse life, we can contact it. Who has not seen an animal or a human, living one minute and dead the next? What has happened during that minute? Certainly something has gone out of the body which one saw in action, and left behind the still flesh which, even as one looks, seems to start to disintegrate and return to Mother Earth. So we can recognize life as a fact, although we may not be able to understand it, and certainly we cannot create it as we can so many other things in these enlightened days. The mind of man has produced many synthetic aids to nature, but not synthetic life.

'The world of science tells us that life is found in all the four kingdoms of nature – the mineral, vegetable, animal and human kingdoms. We do not need to be told that there is life in the animal and human kingdoms – we can see that for ourselves – but it is more difficult to credit that there is life in the mineral and vegetable kingdoms also. Reliable sources tell us that even rocks have life and that when the life-force is withdrawn from such rocks, they commence to decay; in time they crumble and return to the dust, much as a human body does, though the process takes a longer time. It is certainly easier for us to accept the fact that vegetables have life than that rocks have, for when they are withdrawn from the ground, the source of life in their case, we see for ourselves that they wither and die; in due time they become dust, as do all living things when the life-force is withdrawn.

'Philosophers trace life still further into an additional kingdom, which they term the super-human kingdom, for when man has conquered the human kingdom, his evolution does not come to a sudden end, but goes on upwards, ever upwards, until at last it reaches the source from which it sprang, how many countless ages before this one, no mere man has been able even to guess. They state further that life is progressive, as are all things in nature, and that the goal of life is experience; this it garners and harvests as it progresses through the kingdom of nature from the lowest form in which life is found, to the highest, which can be described as the Perfect Man, or a 'man made perfect'.

'Next we must consider what is the difference between life as found in the mineral kingdom and life as we know it in the animal and human kingdoms. Its essence is undoubtedly the same for, as I have stated, the origin of all life is Divine, but how different is its expression. When life starts functioning as various minerals, it has no individuality as we understand such a thing at the human level. In the lower types of minerals the life-force, after having gained the experience it must obtain, passes into the higher forms; later it passes to the lower type of vegetable and so to the higher types of the same kingdom. All this takes many thousands of years as time is reckoned on this planet, but it is only when life passes from the vegetable to the animal kingdom that any sort of division becomes apparent. Even at this stage there is no individuality but merely a group consciousness or group soul, common to all the different animals of the same species, which works on and directs these animals from without. When the life-force passes to the human kingdom, an indwelling spirit or ego inhabits each individual body and dictates the thoughts and actions of every human being. At this stage of evolution group souls have an influence upon races – but none on individuals, who now have free-will.

'To animals man is a super-animal, just as to man a perfect man is a super-man. It is unfortunate to find that this super-animal is inclined to act with cruelty to his younger brothers rather than with compassion and understanding, in fact he seems to be the main cause of the suffering they undergo. If man killed only for the purpose of obtaining food, as animals do, or because a wild animal is threatening to kill him, that might be regarded as conforming to the laws of nature, but he tortures animals by various means so that his women folk may be adorned with furs and feathers, and he kills for what he terms "sport" when he practises his "skill" in marksmanship, regardless of the suffering he may cause to those not so well equipped as himself. All this thoughtless cruelty brings into manifestation the emotion of *fear*, the most retarding of all emotions. Fear of the super-animal begins in the lowest forms of animal life and continues throughout the animal kingdom till animals contact man in domestic life, then the fear that was born in the early stages is slowly but surely replaced by love. Until this happens, the progress of animals along the evolutionary path is slow.

'I shall trace for you the passage of the life-force through the animal kingdom. Try to imagine the life-force as constituting the water of a slowly moving canal; it is bounded on both sides by the banks of the canal, thus giving the impression of a controlled purpose. There is practically no difference in this stream when passing through the mineral and vegetable kingdoms, but there is a distinct change as it emerges from the canal into the conditions ruling in the animal kingdom.'

'The animal kingdom is a complex structure of different levels of evolution, from microbes and worms, through the wild animals of the jungle, to the animals which man has domesticated. In passing through the animal kingdom the life force acquires the colouration of experience. It takes form as, shall we say, myriads of tadpoles. The life-force was contained in the larvae which were produced by a frog; in due course it emerged as many thousands of tadpoles. These were born to contact life and to gain experience which will colour the water that was clear. Many tadpoles die in infancy, never reaching their destiny as frogs, and these units of water may be said to return to the soul groups scarcely coloured at all. Some become frogs, and although through lack of food or for a thousand different reasons their lives may be short, when they eventually come to an end, the units of water comprising these young frogs return to their soul groups, coloured only with the small experience of discomfort or suffering due to the cause of their deaths. Others live longer and in due course contact human life. The frog learns to fear its tormentors, to run from them, to hide when possible and avoid contact with them. In due course, it dies; either by a natural death, which in the majority of cases is unlikely, by the unthinking cruelty of the human kingdom or by an attack from one of the natural enemies of frogs, such as snakes. When the units of water comprising these fragments of life return to the compartments, their experience most certainly colours the water, which when it started out was clear, with many colours expressing sufferings in its diverse forms. The whole experience, blended together, leaves that compartment coloured with the experiences of all the units, none of which has a separate identity, all being part of the complete group soul.

'After one or two lives at this stage of evolution, the life force with its accumulated water experiences passes to the next level. Instead of tens of thousands of tadpoles, it is divided into about ten thousand units of rats, or mice, for example. The rat is born with a fear of the human being and of its natural enemies, for is not the water coloured with the fear that was brought back from the lives lived in the earlier stage. In this series of lives fear continues to grow. In his early life the rat is taught by bitter experience to avoid man at all costs, to work by night when man is less of a terror than by day, and if he manages to live to a ripe old age it is certainly due to his cunning and mastery of methods of circumventing his natural enemies.'

While I was still pondering his final words, I looked up and the room was empty. I sat quite still for a whole and tried to grasp the idea of what he had said, and after a time much of it came back. At first I did not consider whether I believed it or not; that did not seem to matter. It was all so new – but it certainly was interesting; already, although I was tired, I began to look forward to the morrow, for I was confident he would return.

The following day I sat at my desk with my eyes on the door; I was determined I would be on the look-out to see if he opened the door or came through it. But if I expected something supernatural to happen I was disappointed, for just on 11 o'clock the door opened noiselessly in the ordinary way and he greeted me, as I should have expected him to do, just by saying: 'Well, are you ready to hear more, or did I bore you yesterday?' I suppose my reply must have satisfied him, for he continued from where he left off.

'The level of evolution of the life force reached in the wild animals is as far removed from the humble worm, as he is from the plant world. The animals themselves live by the natural law, which is 'the survival of the strongest', and the key-note of the animal kingdom is self preservation. The weaker animals are killed for food, and fear for survival colours the experiences of all such animals from the day they are born to the day they die, whether their death be a natural one or due to the exploitation of the stronger animal or a bullet from the gun of a hunter. Is it any wonder that the predominating instinct of *all* wild animals is fear? Fear of the stronger animals and fear of the super-animal called man.

'Many lives are lived by group souls in the bodies of wild animals, because in such incarnations they learn the important lessons of self preservation and the necessity to work in order to survive, for the obtaining of food alone for each and every animal becomes a daily duty which can never be neglected. During the periods when food is scarce, the instinct of the animal teaches it to seek new pastures and to learn adaptability, which will stand the soul in good stead when the time comes for it to emerge as a separate human entity. Maternal instinct is in evidence for the first time in this stage of the life of the group soul.

'I have said enough for you to realize that the wild animals represent the top of the spiral covering the lives lived by the group soul in the animal kingdom, for when ready to progress further the group soul inhabits bodies that bring it into closer and closer touch with the human kingdom, to which it must pass in the fullness of time.

'In their wild state elephants, donkeys and buffaloes will fight wildly against capture by man, and when caught it is only if they are tamed by kindness that they become at all domesticated and willing to use their natural powers in the interests of human progress. Even after years of captivity they seldom become really domesticated. However in the lives which follow they are mostly born in captivity, therefore their environment from birth teaches them to lose some of the natural fear that past lives have produced in them. The most evolved of this group are the cattle for they are often stall fed in the winter months, and it is generally admitted that the providing of food for an animal does more to gain its confidence and eradicate its natural fear of man than anything else.

'Slowly but surely some of this fear of the human race is obliterated and the group soul is ready to pass into its last stage in the animal world, that of the truly domesticated animals – the horse, the dog and the cat. The group soul which in the beginning went out seeking experience in the form of approximately ten thousand tadpoles has gradually but surely divided itself into fewer and fewer parts, until in the last stages of the animal kingdom it is in two parts only – as two horses, two dogs or two cats.

'When the group soul has evolved to the stage where it is divided in half, it is in every way domesticated and has come to understand man as he really is. Now the possibility of its individualizing as a separate human ego becomes a fact. How many lives still have to be lived by this group soul depends entirely on the human beings to whom these two animals are attached. If one of the two owners of these horses, dogs or cats is *not* an animal lover and therefore the treatment meted out to the animal is unsympathetic, or cruel, then some of the fear which in the last twenty lives has been partly eradicated, will come back again and more lives must be lived before individualization can take place. I cannot emphasize too often or too strongly that if people realized how important it is for them to make friends of all domestic animals and do their part in making them understand man, then this last stage would be reached much more quickly than is often the case.

'Please understand this clearly: *no group soul can individualize into a human soul until all fear of the human race has been overcome.* Love is not an emotion which relates exclusively to the human kingdom, in its highest form it encompasses all nature, therefore man's part in animal evolution is to see that in the true sense "perfect love casteth out fear" for, without understanding help, the progress of animals on the evolutionary path can be retarded for an unlimited period of time.

'How does individualization eventually take place? It can come about in one of two ways – through the pathway of either the heart or the head, which varies with the type of animal. It can be said that a dog most frequently passes into the human kingdom through love and/or sacrifice. Often a dog is so devoted to his master or to the family of his adoption that in an emergency his instinct of self-preservation completely deserts him and he sacrifices his life to save that of his master or a member of the family. It is not essential for either dog to have made the supreme sacrifice of its life for the group soul to individualize; when a dog has learned all the lessons it was meant to learn in the animal kingdom and when all fear of the human race has been eradicated, it would be a waste of time for the group soul to continue with more incarnations in animal form. Its destiny is then elsewhere, so a transfer to a new and more enlightened sphere of existence takes place.

'The first incarnation in a human body is not necessarily passed in a body as undeveloped as the lowest type of human being on the earth, for often the new ego, through having gained much experience in its last few lives in the animal kingdom – especially one who has given up his own life for a human – has earned the right of a human body slightly more developed than the most undeveloped type found in the world.

'A horse individualizes in a way similar to that of a dog – by outstanding devotion to its master. Often one has heard of a horse making a stupendous effort when called upon to do so, only to drop down dead when the effort has been successful.

While a dog or horse passes into the human kingdom through devotion and/or sacrifice, so a cat earns the right to live as a higher

entity by learning to understand man. In olden days many philosophers said that a dog and a horse can earn the right to progress by
devotion whereas a cat employs cunning, the first glimmering of the
faculty of reason.

We can see instances of elephants who have been trained to serve
man, and monkeys who have lived in the right types of zoological
gardens, who obviously qualify in this respect, and in surroundings
devoid of fear they have used their brains and so can be said to
understand, to a limited extent, the ways of man. Animals which
miss out a life as domesticated animals go into the lowest form of
human body that is known in the world. On the other hand, the
group souls of many highly evolved dogs miss out having to inhabit
the bodies of the lowest form of human life known, and are born into
bodies of a more evolved type of man – probably as members of tribes
who for generations have served mankind.

'Before passing on to the early lives of the human race with its
tremendous differences from life in the animal kingdom, I must
mention the case of the animal which individualizes as a human
being whilst still occupying an animal body. The transfer from the
animal sphere to the human must take place when the right time
comes – when all fear is gone, and when the love side of the animal
has been sufficiently developed. In a case where one dog, which is
half a group soul, has died a natural death and where the second
half of the group soul, another dog, remains alive but has no more
lessons to learn, this dog becomes a human being in everything
other than form. Doubtless you have come across cases where a dog
in later life seemed "almost human", where it appeared to understand almost every word that was said to it and where its uncanny
understanding of your thoughts and actions savoured of an intuition beyond what you imagined to be possible in an animal. Such a
dog is in fact a "human dog": an animal in form, but a human in
intelligence and one able to reason and make decisions for which it
alone would be responsible.

'The main difference between a human being and an animal is
the faculty of reason – and with it the gift of free will. A man knows

the difference between right and wrong; even in his early lives as a human being he can make his own decisions, whereas an animal has to obey the laws of the animal world. An animal lives by instinct, and outside the limits of instinct it cannot think. A man can choose the evil path, even though he knows it is evil and against the progressive forces that rule the world, but an animal must ever act as its instinct compels it – for such is the Law.'

Once again I did not see him go, for my mind was so full of these strange ideas. I decided to write down everything I could remember of these two talks and come to the conclusion that I would make shorthand notes of all future talks.

CHAPTER TWO

'So you have been writing down what I have said to you; that is good.'

Today again I had not seen my teacher enter, for I was reading through the notes I had made.

'Yes,' I answered, 'but how did you know what I had been doing?'

'You told me so yourself last night, when you were asleep and out of your body,' he replied.

'I do not propose to explain to you now how you told me last night that you had decided to keep a full record of my talks. When I have finished my visits, you will understand everything so clearly that you will be able to answer such questions yourself.'

He was enthusiastic about my decision to take notes and told me that he would be only too pleased to add to my record of the past two days. I noticed that he did not alter a single word of my script so far as the record had gone, but he spent some little time in filling in the blanks I had left when I could not remember facts exactly.

'You will remember I told you that the keynote of the animal kingdom was self preservation. How different is the keynote of the human kingdom, for it is self sacrifice. Although this is the important standard for any human life, there are other laws which must be understood by those who seek to discover the secrets of the evolutionary path. These are, of course, different from those governing animals and yet, for the first few lives lived by the unevolved man, he is more animal than man. Although he has shaken off his fear of man, the practices brought over from the animal kingdom, where he took what he could by virtue of his brain-power or his physical strength, still persist.

'The first important law which operates in the human kingdom is the law of reincarnation. This law asserts that an ego, once individualized, returns again and again to incarnate in a human physical body until such time as he had learned, by experience in all types of surroundings, all the lessons that can be learned under physical conditions. When the life force progresses through the mineral and vegetable kingdoms, this law exists to a limited extent, but it is not very apparent. In the animal kingdom it also exists, still only to a limited extent as there are as yet no separate entities, but it unfolds itself during the period of evolution after the ego has individualized into the human kingdom.

'The second important law, which operates for humans though not for animals, is the law of karma – often referred to as the law of cause and effect. From the moment that the group soul becomes a separate ego, this law operates. The law of karma decrees that every thought, word or action that emanates from man *must* produce a definite result – either good or bad – and that result must be worked out by us in our lives at the physical level. There is nothing unfair in this, for as the Christian teaching has it, 'as you sow, so shall you reap'.

'According to the law of karma, a selfish act on your part which causes untold misery to another soul, earns a unit of bad karma which must be paid for by your suffering from a similar action at the hand of another, either in this life or in a life to come. In like manner a kind act on your part means that a unit of good karma has been earned by you, the result of which must be either a wiping off of a unit of bad karma made by you – the good offsetting the bad – or the gift of the same amount of kindness from a different source. When a new ego starts his human lives, the number of foolish or evil actions, thoughts and words naturally far exceed those of a beneficent kind and if the law worked literally, the man would lead a life of perpetual misery and suffering, caused entirely by his own actions, thoughts and words, each producing its just result. Such a life would be intolerable and impossible to live; suicide would soon become the practice amongst young souls. A more humane method is adopted however whereby, in any one life, no man is expected to suffer more than he can stand, and the units of bad karma made by him in that life through inexperience, and which have not been paid off or nega- tived by similar units of good karma, are carried forward for working out in future lives. The result of this arrangement, which may be likened to a bank overdraft, is that during the first two hundred or more incarnations the man continually adds to that overdraft. But all this time he is creating what we call the voice of conscience. As that still small voice is built up by the experiences the ego gleans in his different human bodies, it does not operate appreciably for many lives.

'Here is an example: An unevolved man, knowing little of the ways of the human but much of the ways of the animal world, desires to possess something owned by another. His animal instinct is to take that which he desires by force. If he is strong enough he tries to do so; a fight ensues resulting in the death of another human being. The laws governing man then come into force; the murderer is arrested, tried and put to death. The reservoir of knowledge, which exists at the higher mental level, notes the result of such an action and in a *future* life, when the same man in a different body wishes to possess something owned by another, he is warned by the voice of experience, his conscience, that *if* he kills his enemy, he himself will suffer the same fate at the hands of the State. In this manner, gradually, the reservoir of knowledge is built up, each major happening in the lives lived being registered for the purpose of a warning in a life to come. From this simple explanation it can easily be understood that a man who has a sensitive conscience and who listens to it, must be an old soul, for he could not have an effi- cient conscience unless he had much experience in the past lives in which his conscience, or reservoir of knowledge, was built up.

'For perhaps two hundred lives, each life lived produces more units of bad karma than good. Some are paid off in each life through suffering and misfortune, but the balance is transferred to the overdraft. As the ego becomes more evolved (really more experienced) common sense teaches him that evil produces trouble for himself whereas good and kind actions result in happiness and the accumulation of friends. In this manner he evolves to a stage where the number of units of bad karma made in a single life is exceeded by the number of units of good karma earned by good actions: this constitutes a very important stage in a man's development, because from this point on he becomes a really useful and valuable member of society. In all his future lives, before the new incarnation commences, a small percentage of his overdraft is allotted to him for paying off in that particular life, and that quota *must* be paid off, in addition to any units of evil karma made in the life itself. Positive acts of kindness will bring him much happiness and help him along the road.

'In ways such as these, all natural laws can be seen to dovetail one into another, rather like the pieces of a jig-saw puzzle. My task is to present to you the pieces of this puzzle, with which you must eventually learn to make a picture.

'In order that you may understand how it is possible for the members of the human kingdom to gain all their necessary experience, I want you to accept the following propositions:

1 That man is an ego, or soul, and in the course of his evolution from an undeveloped state, the savage, to that of a perfect man, he has to use three vehicles of consciousness or bodies. These are known as the mental or mind body, the astral or emotional body and the physical body; the last is the one which you and I are functioning in and which is visible to the human eye.
2 That these three bodies are used by us when functioning in the three different states of consciousness, which are : the mental plane, the astral plane and the physical plane.
3 That the home of the ego round which these bodies are drawn, is the upper part of the mental world. This is known as the causal level.

'When the ego starts from the causal level for a new incarnation, he has to have one of each of these three bodies. I want you to visualize the ego as a naked man, preparing to clothe himself with his three coverings or bodies. The least dense in texture is the mental body, and this the ego draws round himself from the matter of which the mental world is constructed: this can be likened to the underclothes of a man. The type of mental body that each man gets is in accordance with his mental development at the *end* of his last incarnation, so obviously the mental body of an unevolved man is very different from that of an evolved being, an old soul, one who has had many lives and has gained much experience. The ego next draws round himself a slightly coarser vehicle, made of the matter of the astral world. This body is, as it were, on top of or outside the mental body, and the type of the body is again in accordance with the man's emotional development. The astral body therefore can be likened to the man's suit of clothes. A still coarser and denser body is now required and to obtain this, a body has to be found by physical means at the physical level. In other words, a woman, with the assistance of a man, produces a child. This new physical body is also in accordance with the man's deserts, with his karma made in previous lives. The physical body corresponds to the man's overcoat.

'So every man you see at the physical level is, as it were, wearing three bodies, each one under the other, but owing to the density of the outside body, the physical, it is impossible to see the other two. When a man dies, all that happens is that he drops his physical body – his overcoat. The man is still there, clothed in his astral and mental bodies; the astral being the denser is on the outside, the mental is under the astral. Before I explain what actually happens after death, I must tell you a little more about these bodies.

'The physical body, that which we all see with our eyes, is composed of fairly dense physical matter, but there is also a less dense part of that body, called the etheric double (in ancient Egypt it was referred to as the Ka) which plays a very important part both during the lifetime and at the death of our physical vehicle. It is not a body in the ordinary sense of the word in that you cannot live in it, as you can in your physical body; you cannot even see it, unless you have developed the lowest form of clairvoyance – which is called etheric sight.

'The matter of which this etheric body is composed, also surrounds our nerves. There is a concept of electricity that the current runs not along the wire but along a coating of etheric matter which surrounds it. That is true also of the nerve action of the body; the nerve currents do not actually run along the white thread of the physical nerve, but along a coating of etheric matter which surrounds it, so that if this coating is removed from the physical nerve, we do not get any sensation. This is what happens when an anaesthetic is used. In the case of a local anaesthetic, the etheric matter which conducts the feeling is driven away a short distance from the particular nerve; the white nerve is still there, plain to see, yet when it is cut, the patient feels nothing. When a much more powerful general anaesthetic is given for a major operation, which necessitates the patient being unconscious and devoid of feeling for a considerable time, the etheric matter is driven away almost entirely from the dense body. If it is entirely driven out, then the patient dies; this is what has happened when a patient occasionally dies while under the effect of an anaesthetic. A little too much has been given and the etheric matter which has been driven out cannot get back.

'This etheric matter, gossamer in texture and extremely elastic, which is such an important part of the physical body, has another function. It acts as a liaison or link between the physical and the astral bodies during sleep. When you, the ego, disconnect yourself from your physical body, lying on the bed, a cord of etheric matter attached to your astral body, with its main bulk remaining in and around the physical body, stretches out as you travel to any part of the world that you wish; however far you go this physical link with your body on the bed remains. When the time comes for the body to awaken, an SOS is sent out along this etheric cord to you, wherever you are, and you must return to your physical body and re-enter it; then "wake up" and carry on with your duties at this level.

'When you go to sleep, you, the ego slip out of your physical body at the moment when it loses consciousness; you are clothed in your astral body and living in the astral world, under astral plane conditions. You are free to go wherever you will, leaving your physical body on the bed, where it is resting and gaining strength for the next day's work. It is only the limited physical body which requires rest, in the same way that it requires regular food and drink to sustain it in health and life, you, the ego, need no rest. In your astral body you move about quite easily and can travel to any distance. At the astral level the force of gravity does not exist, so you glide along and it makes no difference whether it is land or sea that you are crossing as you are not affected by either. The distance you can cover in the few short hours that the physical body is resting, is more or less un-limited; when I tell you that you can travel round the world in about two-and-a-half minutes it gives you some idea of the speed that can be attained.

'The astral body, which is composed of much finer matter than the physical one, is drawn round the ego on his way down into incarna-tion. It fills what we call the causal body, forming an ovoid of lumi-nous mist. But the physical body, being denser, has a very strong attraction for the astral matter, and draws this closer to it, so that we have an astral reproduction of the physical form in the centre of that ovoid, and there the astral body is just as recognizable by the features as the physical body, only it is built of finer matter. When the physical body dies, there is no longer any need for the astral body to adapt itself, so the tendency is for it to remain exactly as it was at the time when the physical body ceased to exist, and not grow any larger. The reason for this is that the astral body is not a vehicle with organs, bones, flesh and blood like the physical, but rather a body of mist.

'During his lifetime a man has the opportunity of living under astral plane conditions every time his body is asleep, but in actual fact it is only the man whose standing in evolution is above the average who takes full advantage of these opportunities. The young soul, or unevolved ego, certainly gets out of his body during sleep –

he cannot help doing so – but his intelligence (mental or mind body) is not sufficiently developed to furnish him with the amount of knowledge necessary before he can use all his faculties to their highest extent. Therefore he usually hangs about near his sleeping body, waiting for the call to re-enter it when it has slept long enough and wishes to wake – thus he can never become accustomed to astral plane conditions in the same way as the older ego. When a man of this type dies and no longer has a physical body, he feels that he is in a completely strange world. There are times, immediately after death, when such a man craves for the physical life which he knows, but he can do nothing to regain it – for when the etheric matter has all been withdrawn from a physical body, it cannot be put back.

'Death of the physical body is caused in numerous ways: by illness, when the body finds it impossible to function properly; by old age, when the body is worn out; by accidents in which the vital parts of the body have been irretrievably damaged. In all such cases the etheric part of the physical body has been forced out of the dense part, merely because the dense body can no longer perform its proper functions, and without this body, the etheric double cannot live. At the moment of death, when the heart ceases to beat, the etheric double registers extreme fear and wraps itself round the outside of the astral body in which the man is standing, since he was forced out of the physical body at the time death took place. The etheric part of the physical body knows that the death of the denser part means also death for itself and, in its desire to continue its existence, it clings to the astral body of the man, hoping to survive longer. By an effort of will the man can easily rid himself of this encumbrance. Until he does, he is suspended between the two worlds of consciousness; he cannot function on the physical plane, for he has lost his physical body, and he cannot function properly on the astral plane, because the clinging etheric matter makes it impossible for him either to see or hear properly.

'Men who die fearing death often refuse to make the necessary effort of will, which they are told to make by friends who meet them on the other side, but hang on to the remaining particles of physical matter in the hope of continuing their physical existence, the physical life being the only one they *know*. It is no use fighting of course, for sooner or later they must let go and make the effort of will that I have mentioned – resisting the inevitable only causes them to be suspended between the two worlds for a much longer time than is necessary. A man who has acquired some knowledge of the subject of death by studying cognate subjects during his lifetime, will at once shake himself free from this encumbrance and take up his life again under what I may perhaps call permanent astral conditions. I say 'permanent' because now that he has lost his physical body and will not get another until the time is ripe for him to reincarnate again and spend another short period of time in the physical world, he will be living under astral plane conditions during the day as well as during the night. Immediately the effort of will to get rid of the etheric double is made, the etheric matters falls away and starts to disintegrate in much the same way that the dense physical body disintegrates, but whilst it may be months or years before the disintegration of the physical body is complete, the etheric part of it, being much finer and lighter in weight, returns to dust almost immediately. Now that the physical body is no longer attached, the ego is clothed in his astral body and will function in this body as long as he remains in the astral world.

'The astral world is the world of emotions and illusions; it is composed of matter which is finer than any gas we know, in which are many degrees of density. The astral body is the vehicle of emotions. Emotions are brought about by vibrations of the astral matter; what are known as the higher emotions – love, gratitude, unselfishness and the like – show themselves to clairvoyant vision as vibrations of the finer matter, whilst the lower emotions – greed, envy, jealousy, selfish love (akin to passion) pride etc – show as vibrations of relatively much coarser – or denser – matter. As man is, prior to death, so he will be after death, minus only his physical body and without physical world limitations. His virtues and vices remain the same but, owing to the fluidic nature of the astral body, they become forces of great good or evil. Thus a feeling of slight antagonism at the physical level becomes there sheer hate, with unpleasant results to both parties, whilst one of mild physical affection would draw out a reciprocal outpouring of love which would produce an amazing atmosphere of harmony and peace. As the astral world is the world of illusion, no time or labour need be used as in the physical world; everything – clothes, food etc – is produced by thought. Life there can be one long holiday. We can devote ourselves to whatever we really desire to do and indulge in hobbies to our hearts' content. There are no limitations to prevent us acquiring more knowledge, such as insufficient time to study or the physical limitations of weak sight or a tired body – there is nothing in the astral body which can tire.

'Whilst our physical bodies sleep, we function at the astral level in our astral bodies and there meet friends and relations who have died, so it is foolish to try to forget about these people in the daytime, for they are all around us, the only separation being the limitation of consciousness. In many ways it is a pity so few people remember what they do at night; if they did, they would be much less troubled about the state called death – and the wicked rumours circulated concerning hell and eternal damnation would have no more effect on them than the fear of the ogre in the children's fairy book affects the adult reader.

'Very few people realize that, in the physical world, the average man spends most of his time working in an office or in a shop or on the land, or in some occupation he would not choose had it not been necessary to earn money for food, for drink and for clothes – both for himself and those dependent on him. It is perhaps just as well that so few people *do* realize this, as otherwise we should all be extremely discontented; that would be a hindrance to our evolution and would produce trouble everywhere. Only a few fortunate men are able to earn their living at what they like most. A painter or a musician, even though he be left a fortune, will continue with his work because, generally, his work is part of himself and becomes his pleasure.

'I shall give you a general outline of some of the conditions found on the astral plane. To the man who during his lifetime thought of little else but business, the next life will tend to be rather dull at first, especially if he has been in the habit of loving money for its own sake. Money is a purely physical thing and useless on the astral plane. This type of man will have to develop some other interest if he is to be really happy in the next world. If however a man were fond of music in his lifetime, then he will be fond of it after death and he will find many opportunities of satisfying the longings he was unable to satisfy before. If he wishes, the lover of music can spend the whole of his time listening to the finest music the world can produce. Distance is now no limitation; he may listen to an opera in London for a time, then with scarcely a minute's delay he can be listening to another performance in New York or Australia. He can meet the great musicians of the past – unless they have already reincarnated; he can see the mighty thought-forms which music on the physical plane produces in the finer matter of the astral world. Even though during his lifetime he was unable to play, he can now produce music by imagination. On the physical plane there are many people who are able to imagine beautiful passages of music, but are unable to express themselves owing to the lack of technique. On the astral plane all such people are to be envied indeed, as their natural cravings are for things not dependent on the help of purely physical-plane conditions.

'For the man who is fond of art, all the masterpieces of the world are at his disposal, whether they be in art galleries or private collections. Many an art lover has long wanted to go to Rome. Think of the hours of delight for him devouring the works of art to be seen there and there alone. He may meet the artists of the past, and it must not be supposed that they lose interest in their work because they have died. Far from it, now they create beautiful thought-forms, for they have no longer to use brushes and canvas to express their art. That was their only method of expression in the physical world, but after death the thought-forms they create are just the same as pictures here, just as visible and much more beautiful. Many artists here have stated that they are always dissatisfied with their work when it is finished, even though the world applauds their genius. They often say: 'If only I could express on canvas exactly what my imagination pictures, but never does it come exactly right.' On the astral plane the pictures created are exactly what the artist perceives and so the creations of their imagination there are *more* beautiful than the finest pictures to be found in the world. Lovers of books also have a happy time, for the world's libraries are now open to their inspection.

'As an example of what happens to a man after death, take the sort of person who lives entirely for the physical plane life. By that I do not mean anything bad or that he is a man of many vices. On the contrary he is probably an exceedingly popular man during his lifetime, always surrounded by a host of friends and generally spoken well of by all. Probably his pleasures consist of living well, attending theatres, dances etc. and doing the thousand and one things that go to make up the life of what is termed "a man about town". Undoubtedly he is a successful businessman and considered a model husband, but all the same his life – both business and pleasure – depends on physical things, such as are only obtainable on the physical plane. There are many such people, as everyone who looks around him can see.

'After death a man of this type will probably be extremely bored and will have practically nothing to do. He will soon realize that making thought-forms of good dinners and intricate business deals becomes a very unsatisfactory method of killing time, when there are no physical results. He does not get the physical satisfaction to which he is accustomed after a good dinner with choice wines, though he can imagine and even appreciate the taste of dishes and wines which he used to have on earth. It is impossible for him to feel the same result after drinking alcohol that he felt during his lifetime, however much he may drink, and the feeling of repletion which follows a good dinner on the physical plane is entirely absent from the "astral" meal. Neither does he obtain much satisfaction from a successful business deal produced in his imagination, when he is unable to use the money so made, for on the astral plane things cannot be bought or sold. He can make thought-forms of as many thousands of gold pieces as he likes, but what can he do with them? Nothing! He can be likened to a man who has been wrecked on a desert island, surrounded by treasures, invaluable to him could he transport them to a civilized country, but useless in a place where there are no buyers and nothing to be bought. The man on the desert island has one advantage over the man on the astral plane inasmuch as there is always the possibility of his being rescued, he may be able to return to his country with his newly found wealth. The "dead" man has no such hope, for when he returns to this plane he comes as a child without possessions other than the experience gained in his previous lives, experience stored by his higher self in the reservoir of knowledge which, as he gradually evolves, he is more and more able to bring down to the physical level. Similar dissatisfaction is experienced from his accustomed sports. In all probability he played golf; he can still play golf if he wishes, in his new life, but he soon tires of this, for every shot he makes goes to the exact spot he has in mind at the moment of striking the ball. Every round played is a perfect round, never differing from the one before. Every putt is holed automatically, for he makes a thought-form of what he wishes to do and the fluidic astral matter immediately carries out, in form, the thought that his mind expressed. You can easily imagine how boring such a game would soon become and how different from the games played at the physical level, where one day he would play like a master and perhaps the next would be little better than a rabbit. The uncertainty was the charm of the game, and this no longer exists at the astral level.

'Consider the man who all his life has been taught that hell-fire and eternal damnation are the portion of all who do not come up to the standard of perfection demanded. After death the difficulty of ridding himself of such thoughts causes him to go through much misery. He is continually tortured by the thought that he is being fooled, although assured that such beliefs are untrue. Until he manages to discard them he will be unable to settle down in the new life, where there is so much to be seen and to be learned.

'There are others who are miserable when they look back on their physical life from this higher level they realize the number of opportunities they have wasted. This reacts on them in different ways. Some are filled with remorse; others, more sensible, make up their minds not to waste their opportunities next time. Again we find a man who has been supporting a wife and a large family before his death. Probably he has not made adequate provision for them and he worries how they will manage. This is a very natural thing, but unfortunately it is a very foolish one too. Having laid down his physical body he no longer has any further responsibility at the physical level. No worrying can bring practical help and it reacts on those left behind in a way that makes them more depressed than they need be. He is adding to their troubles instead of lessening them, and a solution of the problem only comes about when he realizes that those he has left behind are separate egos each working out his or her karma, and that probably this trouble they are passing through is an opportunity to pay off some of the bad karma which has to be worked off during this particular lifetime.

'There are people in this world who always make trouble for themselves, by worrying about things over which they have no control or by being pessimistic about the future – always feeling sure that the worst will happen. After death such men are the same; they continue to feel depressed and to radiate depression wherever they go. Unfortunately, people with these depressing ideas continue to flock together as they did on the physical plane and still believe what they previously believed although the lie is, as it were, before their eyes. Sooner or later men of this type are made to realize their foolishness by those who are ever on the watch for opportunities to help such sad cases; the new teacher must then fill in the gaps he has made through taking away that which he condemned, by offering something more reasonable, more comforting – something which explains not only the present, but the past and future.

'Never spurn an idea because is is strange to you; rather listen to all sides of the question and draw your own conclusions. Your mind may temporarily become chaotic, but out of the chaos you may find light, the light which will set your feet upon the path that ultimately will lead you to knowledge, and on to the wisdom of the perfect man. Get rid of the idea of reward or punishment. There is no reward, no punishment, but there is result, there is cause and effect, and the Law acts just as much in higher worlds as it acts down here on the physical plane. As we live now and as we are now, so shall we be on the other side of death, and our life there will be conditioned by the thoughts with which we have surrounded ourselves down here. So let us take an intelligent interest in higher things, science, art, music, literature and the beauties of nature, in fact anything which is not purely physical, and in the next world we shall have a happy life and be in a position to enjoy opportunities which would be useless to us had we not prepared ourselves by our life here.'

CHAPTER THREE

'Yesterday I began to give you a brief outline of conditions as they exist on the astral plane – and I shall continue with this today.

'The theory of the great church of Rome, stated very roughly and briefly, is that after death the hopelessly wicked drop into an eternal hell immediately; whilst the very great saints go at once to heaven. The ordinary man, neither very good nor very bad, needs a long or short stay in an intermediate condition – called Purgatory – in which his faults are eliminated. As I have told you there is no such thing as an eternal hell – there could not be, if for no other reason than that a finite cause can never produce an infinite result – and those who pass to the astral plane with the fear of this in their minds, go through a difficult beginning stage. There is little more foundation for the statement about the very great saints, for there is a condition called the heaven world and it is quite possible that a very few great saints glide rapidly through the intermediate world, the astral, and pass directly to the mental world, there to continue their evolution. For the very large majority of people the question of going to either heaven or hell does not arise, their mode of progress is by passing through two conditions, the lower of which is known as purgatory and it is with purgatory that I wish to begin today.

'The Roman Catholic doctrine of purgatory as an intermediate condition in which faults are eliminated by a rather painful process – symbolized by burning in fire – has a great deal of truth in it but it is entirely deprived of its dignity by the ridiculous theory of indulgences, the suggestion that man can buy himself out of this inconvenient stage without learning the lessons for which that stage exists. There is of course no possibility of such a thing; no number of thousands of pounds could make the slightest difference to what happens to a man after death. Money may help him to circumvent the laws of the physical plane during his lifetime, but after he has left this world, money has lost its value and such expenditure by friends and relations remaining in the world, so far as he personally is concerned, is wasted. It has always seemed to me a ridiculous thing to suggest that money can divert a law of nature. You cannot divert the law of gravity by offering it money, nor can you turn aside the law of divine justice by bribing it with candles, prayers and offerings.

'This purgatory as it is called, not at all inaptly because it is a state of consciousness where a great deal of refinement and improvement takes place, is in the lower planes of the astral world – that part into which man passes almost immediately after death. It is the region where a man is purged of the blinding lower desires which would keep him indefinitely bound to his desire body. Evolution requires that he move on to higher regions; in order that he may do this, he passes through spheres where he is made to suffer in the same way that he has made other people suffer in his physical life – through dishonesty, cruelty and so on. Through time and suffering he learns the importance of honesty, justice, tolerance, etc., and, having accomplished this, moves on. In his next incarnation he will be born free from sin – although the tendency to succumb to the same desires is still there – and every evil act he commits in that life will be one of free will. A man will continue in this way until he has learned by bitter purgative experiences that he must practise tolerance and do good to others regardless of how he is treated in return. Certain eternal laws have been established and we must try to understand them as such. If there were no laws of nature, we should soon be in a chaotic condition, with nothing on which we could depend; but there *are* laws of nature and these laws are the expression of the Divine Will.

'I shall try to explain what happens in purgatory by giving you some examples: The example which is always given first, because it is the most easily comprehended, is the case of the man who has yielded, in excess, to the curse of drink – the *drunkard*. We all of us know what this drink curse can be; we know of so many cases where a man has wrecked his life, starved his wife and children and even committed crimes innumerable, simply and solely to gratify his craving for the sensation that drink produces. If a man drank only to quench his thirst, then he would have no desire for drink after death – for thirst, like hunger, is unknown in the astral world – but the origin of the desire is not thirst, it is the *craving for a certain pleasurable sensation*. After death the same craving which drove him in his lifetime to such terrible lengths will be stronger than ever, but now that he has lost his physical body there will be no possibility of satisfying it. Desire does not belong to the physical body only, or even principally, it belongs to and is one of the functions of the desire vehicle. The other names of the "astral plane" are the "desire plane" and the "emotional plane" and in this plane desires and emotions are undiluted; the full force of a desire now tears at a man who, in his physical body, has only felt about a hundredth part of the strength of real desire. No one can deny that this is suffering, but also no one can say that the man is being punished. All that has happened is that the law of cause and effect has come into operation and he is now reaping as he sowed; he is now feeling the result of his actions during his lifetime – but he is not being punished. He has set up in himself a desire and so he suffers; the time during which the suffering lasts may well seem to him an eternity, though in reality it may be only a few days, a few weeks or a few months. To a certain very limited extent he can gratify his desire in imagination. He can make thought-forms of drink and imagine he is drinking. He can even imagine the taste of the liquid, but he cannot produce the result, the sensation for which he drank during his lifetime. The nearest that he can get to this sensation is to go to places where people are drinking and suck up, as it were, the fumes of the alcohol, which gives him a very limited amount of satisfaction. He does not get much, but it is something and the best that he can get now that his physical body is no more.

'So here we have the case of a man who, did he relate his

experiences, would certainly say that he was thrown into hell indeed. Not eternal of course, but quite long enough and sufficiently painful whilst it lasted, to make him think of that period as an eternity. The trouble is that no one can really help such a man; that is to say, in the sense of preventing this experience from happening. The only thing that can be done is to explain carefully to him what is happening and the reason for it all, and tell him that the only way out is to get rid of the desire, for until it has worked itself out or been got rid of, the suffering must continue. Sooner or later he realizes this and so that stage of his purgatory ends.

'Next, take the case of a *miser* who hoards his gold on earth and secretes it so that he alone knows where it may be found. Think of the pleasure he derived, whilst living, from visiting the venue of his hoard and gathering up the gold pieces or notes, letting them slip from his fingers one by one, to fall again on the heap which he has made. Picture his crying out in his joy; "All mine, all mine, and no one shall touch it but me." Then think what such a man's feelings would be when he saw from the astral level the hoard discovered, and probably spent recklessly by those who were fortunate enough to find it. He could do nothing, although doubtless he did hang round the hiding place for a considerable time after death. He may have tried to influence the searchers to go elsewhere; no doubt he did all in his power to put them off the scent, but he would know no method of communicating with them, except when they were asleep and temporarily at his level. In most cases they would remember nothing of such conversations and so be uninfluenced by his efforts. Once again, no one is punishing that man, nevertheless he is suffering from the uncontrolled emotions of *covetousness and greed*. He must get away from purely physical things if he is to find happiness.

'Another very common case is that of the extremely *jealous* man who thinks he is in love with someone, whilst in reality all he wants is to possess that individual, body and soul, for his own personal gratification. Surely a man who really loved would be thankful to see the object of his love receive admiration and attention from others, but the jealous man is not. Having been jealous during his lifetime, he remains jealous after death, torturing himself indefinitely and uselessly by constantly watching the approaches of others to the object of his supposed love, hating those other people and trying in every way to influence them, but finding his efforts useless. No one is punishing such people for being jealous; they are simply reaping the results of their own foolishness through the uncontrollable operation of the law of karma – or the law of cause and effect. The only way that anyone can help them is by the intellectual method of giving them advice, trying to show them how foolishly they are acting, and by explaining to them that all that is required for them to obtain peace is that they should eliminate the *selfishness* from their love and should realize that no one can own another ego, body and soul, however much he may wish to do so.

'One other example and then I am finished with purgatory. A businessman once ruined one of his competitors and when criticized by some of his friends, said that harsh treatment was good in business, that he had learnt the hard way and that the lesson would not be wasted on his competitor in the long run. Sure enough, after some years had elapsed, the broken man did rise again – in fact he became a much more successful man than the one who had ruined him in his early life. The ruthless man often quoted this as proof of how right he had been – that ruthless treatment of a competitor was in reality a blessing in disguise. He thought no more about the incident during his lifetime.

'How different it all appeared when the whole story was shown to him in what is called purgatory. There he saw the little man after he was ruined, return to his home where he told his wife of his misfortune. It was also shown how this man's son, who was starting his career at the University, had to give up that career and take the first job offered to him – that of a humble clerk. The father started again and, as I have said, in due time became a rich man, but that was too late to help the son. What of him? He was bitter at the trick Fate had played on him, so instead of settling down in his new sphere of activity and making the best of it, he became mixed up with bad companions, tried to make money quickly by dishonest means and finally landed in prison, which broke his mother's heart and caused her death. The whole story, now seen in its full perspective, is a major tragedy, and you can easily imagine the suffering of that ruthless businessman when he realized that the result of his *greed*, so thoughtless at the time, caused not only the temporary ruin of a small competitor but also the death of one woman and the ruin of a young man's career.

'On the other side, we see the full and complete results of all our actions; few of us do not suffer in the seeing and register a vow that in future lives we shall act differently. The change in outlook towards such things is what purgatory is meant to produce and once our outlook is changed, our experiences in purgatory are at an end. By learning these lessons thoroughly, we can ensure that after future lives our passing through the lower part of the astral world will be little delayed by experiences similar to those I have related. We have to learn a lesson once only and if our characters change thereby, we avoid much trouble and temporary misery in the future.

'Just as the astral experiences of the average man and the man below average standard are in accordance with the types of lives they have lived on earth, so those of the *intellectual man*, the man above the average, are also in accordance with his mode of living. Such men pass more quickly through the lower to the higher levels of the astral world, where they are not only able to continue any experimental work in which they were interested, but can gather students with similar tastes round them. Such gatherings are to be seen frequently; the scientists with his group of students, the mathematician with his smaller group, both find the astral world a much more suitable plane in which to work than the physical world, for four dimensional space can now be studied with opportunities of experimenting. The artist has his group of pupils trying to imitate his skill, as also does the musician, and now the latter is happy indeed for he has the opportunity of listening not only to the world's music but to the music of nature from that of the sea and the wind to the music of the spheres – for there *is* a music of the spheres, there *is* an ordered song as the planets move through their mighty curves in space. There is music and colour connected with all the vast cosmic world, but as yet we understand the glory of the cosmic life as little as the crawling ant understands our life, with its many activities. A musician may meet the great angels of music, for there are angels who live for music, who express themselves in and by music, to whom music is what speech is to us. You will hear more about their activities later.

'For the *spiritually minded man*, the man who has meditated deeply on higher things, there waits an infinity of bliss. During his lifetime he has had to rely on faith and his own reasoning powers, now he can prove the truth of many of the theories which he has studied in the world, and one can but faintly imagine the joy and peace that this knowledge will bring to such a man; he has been struggling in darkness and now, to a certain extent, he has found the light.

'The philanthropist who during his lifetime has had one thought, one object in view – the helping of his fellow men – has perhaps the greatest opportunity of all, for now he is free to devote the whole of his time to helping and comforting those who require his services. If he takes up the special work of helping those who have just passed over, he will find work for every minute of his astral life. During war time the need for this work is great, for the ignorant are many and the helpers are few. Much good karma is then earned by those who have fitted themselves for such work and who seize this golden opportunity.

'Therefore I say to you, seek knowledge, not that you may help yourself alone, but that by this knowledge you may be able to assist your brother in distress, also that you may take your share in this great scheme of evolution and be, what every thinking man should be, a guide and a helper to the ignorant.'

'Today brings me to one of the most pleasant parts of my description of the astral world, for I must now talk about children, and after all do not children really make a world? It is only necessary to spend Christmas with a family that is without children to realize what a difference their happy voices and romping games make to this greatest of all festivals; nothing seems the same, the house appears to be dead and the world empty of true happiness. Children's laughter is the most wonderful thing in the world, the one thing most missed by those who have worshipped at its shrine in the past, when they find that the time is gone by and that the revellers of the nursery have been submerged into the huge cauldron of adult humanity. It is as if children are the only really natural beings in the human world – the only people who understand enjoyment.

'The explanation of this lies in the fact that having so recently returned to earth they are as yet so near to the truly glorious life of the heaven-world that they still retain some touch with life at its highest, life that is one with the nature kingdom, the land of fairies, the land of beauties untold and undreamed of by the material beings we all seem to become when we grow up and are tarred with the brush of convention and "respectability". A condition analogous to this is to be seen in the animal kingdom. Even lion cubs are delightful as babies; when they are born, they have no fear for they have just come from the astral world where fear does not exist for them. After some months, or even a year or so, their instinct – which is part of the group soul to which they belong – filters through, then fear and antagonism for the human race comes into force and no longer can they be considered as safe pets.

'It is usually considered that nothing is quite so sad as for a child to be cut off at any stage of its career, but especially at the time when it is emerging from babyhood into what is described as the 'interesting stage' at about three years old. The period when a child ceases to be a child is not determined by age; some lose their childish ways as soon as they enter school, others remain children till well into their teens. The death of a child must always seem unnecessary to those who have not grasped at least the elementary theory of evolution, for it is very natural that they should wonder why parents have to suffer in this way, and what the use is of a life which ends so soon after it has begun. Students of evolution however realize that a child is an individual who has descended to this physical plane to obtain experience – to work out its destiny. If it dies young, it gains little experience and it will not take long to assimilate this after leaving the physical world, thus it is more likely that the child who has died young will be the sooner back to live another life. It does not follow that it would lose anything or suffer in any way from this early death. If the average person would only take the little trouble necessary to gain this knowledge, how much happier the world would be.

'When a baby is about to pass to the next world, the ceremony of baptism should always be performed. This rite makes the child a member of a holy brotherhood, surrounds it with a certain definite protection and starts it along a certain line of vibrations and influences which prevent harm from coming near it.

'When children reach the astral world they have a wonderfully happy life, because of the absence of restrictions. They never lack attention for there are always numbers of mothers that have passed over who are willing and eager to care for a child that has died when a baby. They have the same maternal feelings when living at the astral level as they had when living in the physical world. Poverty, lack of food, suffering from cold – such things have no place in the thoughts of the astral mother. Sleep is no longer a necessity, so there is plenty of time to give to any child she adopts. Apart from the pleasure of seeing that it is cared for and amused, she can commence the child's education, introducing it to the beauties of this world in their many forms. Such teaching may leave its mark on the child and may cause it to turn to the artistic side of life in its next incarnation. As well as foster-mothers, who are *always* available, there is a vast army of astral helpers also ready to pilot a new-comer through the early stages of his new life.

'Like the adult, the child is unchanged by passing to this new world. There are always many who are only too anxious to help him at his games and there are also the nature-spirits, who play a great part in children's games on the astral plane. Think of the imaginative child surrounding himself, still in imagination, with the wonders of the kingdoms described in his fairy books. In this astral world the child will not have to rely on make-believe. Once a thing is imagined, it is there plain for him to see, for the matter of the astral world is moulded by thought, and just as long as the child imagines a thing so will the thing be there. Instead of sitting in an old wash-tub with a pair of walking sticks for oars, the child who wants to row on the river has only to think of the river, only to imagine the boat and the oars, and they are there for his use. The child who loves to imitate the heroes of fiction has only to think strongly of himself as the hero and he immediately becomes his idea of what that character should be. The plastic astral body is moulded into that very shape and so for the time being, the child absolutely becomes what he is trying to imagine. He becomes Hermes with the winged shoes or Jason in charge of the Argo or Robin Hood, the hero of Sherwood Forest. Whatever he thinks of, he becomes and when he gets tired of that impersonation, he has only to think of someone else and the plastic astral body obeys his commands. It is a wonderful education for a child, this living amongst the characters of his imagination, since he learns much by this method that would be impossible under physical plane conditions.

'We all know the child who is continually asking questions: how often have we found ourselves up against a stumbling block, because it is impossible to give an answer that may be understood by the listener who has only a child's undeveloped brain and elementary intellect. Sometimes we even go so far as to scold the child and try to discourage him from questioning. We do not want to hinder his progress, we just feel that now and again our answers are so inadequate that it would be better for the question to remain unanswered rather than to give a wrong impression. When the astral plane conditions can be made use of, all that is changed. He can be shown the answer to his question by making an image to float before his eyes. A living model (for it is living so long as our thought is concentrated upon it) is a great improvement on a wordy discourse.

'It may be asked: "Do the children not miss their fathers and mothers, friends and playmates?" No they do not and for this reason. Everyone when asleep spends these hours in the same world as the child who is dead. The fathers and mothers who mourn because they think they have lost a child, find that the same child is visible to them again the moment they sleep and are out of their physical bodies; they are able to talk to the child and he to them, to play with him, to continue his education and so on. They are able, practically, to carry on from where they left off on earth, but the pity of it is that these self-same parents remember nothing about this when they wake up in the morning. The child after death is invisible to the average parent – to all who have not developed clairvoyance – whereas the parents are never invisible to the child. He can always see them (the astral counterparts of their physical bodies) and often when parents are mourning over the death of a child, the one who is dead is standing by their side, trying in every way possible to communicate with them. To the child, the parents seem to be very dull and stupid at such times, for the child cannot realize that although he can see them, they cannot see him.

'An oft repeated question is: "Do children grow when they are living in the astral world?" This question is always difficult to answer, because if the child is asked, it usually answers: "Yes, I have grown quite a lot." As I have told you, the astral body does not grow after death, for though the child develops mentally and learns more, the body actually remains as it was when the child died. Growth is only necessary at the physical level; after a person is born, the body grows gradually until it attains full stature, unless the subject dies when physical growth automatically ceases. As there is now no physical body to which the astral body need adapt itself, it too ceases to grow. When the child says it has grown, it means the child "thinks" it has grown; the plastic astral body immediately responds to that thought and for a time *is* bigger, but as soon as the thought is dropped, the body returns to its actual or usual size. There is nothing mysterious about this; it is only the working of the laws of nature, and higher matter responds to those laws as well as the lower variety.

'I once saw a most interesting example of how this works for different people, in a case where a man and his wife died together in a motor accident. Ten years previous to that date they had lost a young daughter aged five. The man who had studied occultism expected to see his daughter looking just the same as when she was alive, so greeted her by picking her up in his arms in the same way as he used to do when he came home from his office. The wife, however, not having studied these matters in any way, naturally added up the years that had passed since the child died and expected to see a girl of fifteen years of age waiting to greet her on the other side. She was not disappointed; she saw the tall girl with the attractive face and eyes that she had so often imagined her daughter would grow into and exclaimed as she greeted her: "Haven't you grown! Why, you're nearly a woman now." The husband, knowing something of the peculiarities of the astral plastic matter, was not at all surprised and did not spoil her pleasure by explaining to his wife that what she was really seeing was a thought-form made by herself, within which was housed the ego of their daughter whom they had not seen, except during sleep, for the past ten years. This example shows that although it is a fact that people do not grow in size on the astral plane, yet to those who cannot subscribe to this fact or find it difficult to understand, their illusions prove quite satisfactory and no one is harmed by them.

'Before finishing my remarks on the life of children at the astral level, let me give you one example to show how the early death of a child can and usually does benefit that child considerably. Two people who were married but in poor circumstances, longed for a child. In due time a son was born to them who lived for just two years. The parents were frantic with grief at his loss and nothing and no one seemed to be able to console them. Life which before had seemed to be nearly perfect, was now empty and desolate and the atmosphere of their home was depressing in the extreme. In time they felt the loss less keenly but the wound was still there, and each made it worse for the other by treating the subject as a closed one, never to be mentioned – which only meant that they both brooded all the more in their inner hearts. The one thing they had both loved, the child whose future they had planned, had been taken from them and great was their grief, great their feeling of frustration, that they should be treated thus by a creator who was said to be beneficent.

'This sorrow acted in different ways on the two people: whilst the woman carried on her household duties and prayed that one day she might conceive another child, the man threw himself whole-heartedly into his business, feeling quite rightly that hard work would take his mind off his great sorrow. Five years after the death of the first child, the woman produced another son and their joy was complete. As it happened the new son was the same ego who had been taken from them five years ago. Through the hard work which the sorrowing father had put into his business the material re-sources of the family were now flourishing, so when the time came for the second child to be educated, the man was in a position to give him a first class education – five years earlier the money would not have been available for this.

'The net result of this seemingly useless death was that firstly the husband and wife paid off quite a number of units of karma through their suffering and secondly the child who had earned the right to be given a good education by actions in his previous life, had to be with-drawn from the first body, kept waiting five years for the second body and then reborn to the same family. The child ego did not suffer at all by these occurrences; he gained much by the opportunities avail-able to him in his second body. Being born a few years later is nothing in the scheme of evolution, but often a few years make all the difference to the conditions ruling in a particular family on the physical plane, which can have far reaching effects on egos born into such environment.

'To sum up. Generally it is necessary for a man to return to the home of the ego, which is at the higher mental level, only if he has lived a life in the physical world for an average length of time. To get there he must pass through the astral world, live his life there, then drop his astral body and in his mental body consolidate at the mental level all the mental experiences and intellectual efforts that took place in his last life. This being done, his mental body is also dropped and he does not get new mental and astral vehicles until the time comes for him to incarnate again. I mention this now so that you may realize that a short life on the physical plane often means that the child, having little or no experience to consolidate after such a short physical existence, returns to the astral plane only, for a few years, and is then given a new physical body retaining the same astral and mental bodies which it had drawn round itself prior to the recent short life on the physical plane.

'As you are beginning to appreciate, evolution is a slow process; we would understand it more easily if we could see the scheme as a whole instead of the small part most of us get a glimpse of whilst living at the physical level.

'There is much that I shall have to teach you about life at the astral level, and I shall give you an opportunity of asking as many questions as you like concerning the points on which you are not quite clear. Before I go on however I propose to try out an experiment, with which I think you will be only too anxious to co-operate. Last night I received permission from my Master who is one of the great adepts or perfected men who help to govern this planet, to give you the opportunity of seeing for yourself some of the conditions about which I have been talking the last few days. It was my Master who sent me to you in the first place.

'What I propose is that you shall yourself go on an astral journey and, if you will do exactly what I tell you, I think I can help you to remember much of that which you see and do during the time you are out of your body. Tomorrow morning therefore I shall not visit you as I usually do. You can spend the morning reading all the notes you made of my talks during the past six days. Refresh your memory on every detail possible, for you will need to remember a great deal of what I have told you if you are to benefit from the opportunity I propose to give you, in the hope that it will make many things which are now not clear, easier for you to understand.

'You must eat no meat today or tomorrow nor touch alcohol. I know you usually eat very little meat and seldom drink very much, but even a little alcohol will add to my difficulties, for it will be my job to impress on your brain cells, on your return to your physical body, the necessity for you to remember what you have been doing out of your body. It may not necessarily be completely successful, but we shall try, and since my Master has agreed to the scheme, I have no doubt that He will help me to carry it out. Tomorrow evening you must have your last meal at 7 o'clock; go to your room after dinner and be ready for bed at 9.45 p.m. I have here a tablet which you must take when you go to bed, as it will ensure that you are asleep by 10 o'clock, at which time I shall arrive. Before settling yourself for sleep, try to imagine what you look like lying on your bed. The simplest method of doing this is for you to imagine that, immediately above your bed, where the ceiling is, there is a huge mirror. Were this so, what would you see in that mirror after you got to bed? That is the picture I wish you to have in mind as you fall asleep, for that is what you will see immediately after you disconnect yourself from your physical body.

'At first you may be so surprised at seeing what appears to be you lying on the bed (whereas the real you is looking at that physical body) that instinctively you become somewhat frightened and the result of that fear would be a hurried return to the body on the bed and you would wake up again. I am warning you beforehand what to expect, as I wish to avoid this. Although you get out of your body every night, you do not remember anything about this because you are not conscious of getting out; now I am trying to arrange that there will be no break of consciousness at all between your falling asleep and *realizing* your detachment from your physical body. I shall try to help you to retain that continuity of consciousness, right from the moment of your falling asleep to the moment of your return to your body in the morning. Then you will have no difficulty in remembering and being able to describe in detail all you have done in your astral body during the hours when your physical body remained lying on the bed. Without this continuity of consciousness, you would remember little or nothing of such doings, only bringing back a fragment of one or more happenings, which you would probably describe as a dream. Most peoples' dreams are fragments of what they have been doing during their sleep which the brain cells often distort. It is never easy to remember every detail correctly and it takes years of study, concentration and practice to achieve anything like perfect results. That is why I cannot guarantee that you will remember everything, even when helped by my Master: if perchance you *are* entirely successful you must not be disappointed if you find, as undoubtedly you will, that on future occasions, when you wake up, you are unable to bring through anything at all.

'Now I will leave you until we meet tomorrow night. The day after tomorrow I shall not see you either, because I wish you to write down all you can remember of your astral experiences: we shall discuss these when I see you again in the flesh in three days' time, at the usual hour. Have faith in yourself, and all will be well.'

CHAPTER FOUR

Part of my instructions were that I should write down everything I could remember about last night's happenings. This sounds simpler than it proved to be, for I can tell you at once that the experiment was successful in every way. I do not know if I have remembered everything that happened – I expect my teacher will tell me that today – but I have remembered so much that I have had to marshall my thoughts very carefully to get it written down.

It was a dark moonless night; I went to bed at 9.45 p.m. as I had been instructed, took the tablet which had been given to me and concentrated on imagining what I would see in a mirror above my bed. I have a little French clock which stands beside my bed; it is a great treasure of mine, for it cost a small fortune when I bought it as an impecunious undergraduate at Cambridge. It chimes both the quarters and the hours with a soft silvery note that has never either stopped or interfered with my sleeping. I had heard it strike a quarter to ten, for then I had taken my tablet. It was just when I heard the first silvery chime starting to herald in the four quarters preceding the striking of 10 o'clock, that I seemed to feel something quite unusual going on in my body. Something inside it seemed as if it were loose and I felt what I can only describe as a sliding movement, which I suppose was really myself slipping out of my physical body, for before the clock had started to record its ten strokes, I found myself suspended in space and looking at my body lying on the bed, exactly as I was told I would do – only I was not standing on the floor but perhaps a foot above it (it was really later when I realized this had been so). When I became aware of existing apart from my body, my heart seemed to palpitate, but I cannot say I was exactly frightened and I certainly did not have any desire to rush back. To say I was surprised is putting it mildly; I was excited, I was thrilled, there was a semblance of fear also, a fear of the unknown, a fear of the unusual.

To my astonishment it was as light as day! This was my first realization of the light which rules everywhere and all the time at the astral level, and although I hardly noticed its character at the time, I found later that it is a bluey-grey light; if you can imagine what a room looks like just after dawn is breaking – only much lighter – it will give you some idea of the appearance of my room. I heard a merry laugh behind me, which oddly enough did not startle me at all. I turned round, and there was Charles looking exactly the same as when I had seen him last. Obviously he was enjoying my surprise and my incredulous expression, and his face was wreathed in smiles with all the jolly old wrinkles that I knew so well showing as in the days that were gone. Automatically I clasped him by the hand, at once I felt that his handclasp was as firm and as real as it used to be. My Indian friend whom I had not noticed before but who was also in the room, said: 'Yes, he is real all right, as I told you, and because you are using at the moment the same type of body as he is using, he naturally is as real to you as you are to him.' My joy at seeing Charles was so great that I suppose I spent quite a minute or two shaking him by the hand, putting my hands on his shoulders and altogether satisfying myself that he was really there – 'in the flesh' I should have described it. I found it difficult to appreciate that although the astral body looks like the physical so far as features are concerned, yet it is not in any way physical and has no flesh, bones or tissues. However, Charles was real enough for me and I started asking him a thousand and one questions, such as one does with a person one loves and whom one has not seen for some time. I wanted to know how he was, what he was doing, was he happy etc., and when he could get a word in edgeways, he quietly said: 'Don't you worry, I'm all right and having a good time, as you will see for yourself.' I commented on his still wearing uniform. 'Oh, am I?' he replied, and went on to say that he had not thought about what he was wearing. My Indian friend then explained that I saw Charles dressed in his uniform because that was what he was wearing the last time I had seen him and so I, unknowingly, had made a thought-form of him dressed in his uniform, and the plastic astral matter had immediately responded to my thought. He told me also that even if Charles had thought about what he was wearing before seeing me, I should not have seen him dressed in the type of clothing he had imagined, unless he had mentioned it to me. I would always see him dressed as *I* imagined he would be.

My Indian friend then asked me what I would like to do. Charles suggested that we start with an astral dinner and asked me if I would like to go to the Trocadero Grill, which was a favourite haunt of ours when we were in England together. Naturally I said 'Yes,' wondering how it would be managed, but having seen Charles alive – very much alive in fact – I felt that nothing was impossible. 'Come along then, let's go,' said Charles and began to leave the room. I went to open the door and Charles immediately started pulling my leg about it. He explained that I would have to get accustomed to going through doors on the astral plane without bothering to open them and, although it seemed strange, I found that this was so, for the door offered no obstacle to my passage. As my bedroom is on the first floor, I started going down the stairs in the usual way. I noticed that Charles, who was ahead of me, did not use the steps at all, but just floated down, a foot or so above them – and I found I could do the same. This floating about was certainly a strange sensation at first, but the absence of the force of gravity, to which we are so accustomed at the physical level, soon proved a great advantage and one which one gets used to very quickly.

We set out at what seemed a pretty fast pace. I kept close to Charles and my Indian friend was on the other side of me. I asked Charles how he knew the way to England, to which he replied that you soon get used to finding your way about. We passed over the harbour, travelling about ten yards above the sea. I looked round and saw the lights of Colombo fading in the distance, then for a few seconds we did not seem to be passing anything at all. It was difficult to distinguish the actual places that we passed, for almost as soon as they came into view on the horizon, we had passed them. Apart from this fact the sense of amazing speed was hardly noticeable for there was no head-wind such as one notices at high speeds in the physical world. There did not seem to be any resistance at all and I found later that there is none, for the astral matter is so fine in texture that passing through it at what must be terrific speed, compared with what we are used to here, makes no difference at all.

In about the same time that it has taken me to describe this journey, we came to land, which Charles informed me was 'Old England'. He told me that we had taken more or less a straight course, for naturally it was unnecessary to make any deviations, as land or sea made no difference to travel under astral conditions. When we reached England, which I recognized when we slowed down over Dover, I became fascinated with the ease with which we moved. It is difficult to describe in ordinary language, but if you can imagine what it would be like if you were able to travel at any speed you wished, merely by expressing a thought to that effect, that should give you some idea of the process. We had gone up higher as we approached the land and now we floated some yards above the tallest houses over London.

We had left Ceylon shortly after 10 p.m. – which was 5.30 p.m. in England. We came down to street level when we were over Hyde Park. I knew it was still daylight for no lights were showing, but the light of the astral world was just the same here as in the East, where it was night time. I commented on this and was told that as the astral body never requires rest, there is neither night nor day at the astral level. This was one of the first interesting points of difference between the two worlds which made an impression on me. Charles suggested that I might like to go along Oxford and Regent Streets, to see how it felt to walk in my astral body. To be walking along Oxford Street where I had not been since 1939, just before the outbreak of war, was indeed intriguing. The street was thronged with people, as one would expect it to be at this time of day; although the pavements were crowded, this did not seem to make any difference to us because we actually walked *through* people in their physical bodies who were travelling in the opposite direction to us. It is not strictly correct to say that we were unaware of walking through them, for we felt as if we were passing through a small cloud of mist when we did so; for a moment we were enveloped in it, then we were through it and everything around us was clear. The mist did not in any way impede our progress, but we did feel it, and in a similar way when we came into contact with other people using their *astral* bodies, we felt them to a slight extent though they did not in any way hinder us. In the world I have often seen a person shudder and in a joking way say that someone was walking over his grave. I know now that this sensation must have been caused by a physical body coming into contact with an astral entity which, although the astral matter is too fine in texture to interfere with the physical body passing through it, leaves a slight impression.

I thought that my Indian friend must look rather unusual in these surroundings in his Eastern clothes, so mentioned this to him. He replied: 'I do not suppose you know that I have changed my clothes; if you will look at me now, you will see that I am dressed in a similar way to the Europeans we see around us.' I did look, and it was so. His turban was no longer there and, as his skin was almost as white as ours, he looked very much like one of the Indian students who are so often seen in London. Because he mentioned it, I saw him as he had imagined himself. He explained that one soon gets used to changing one's clothes, as circumstances make such changes desirable; the plastic astral body immediately obeys the thought, even as it is made.

I said I would like to stroll into Selfridges, which we were passing at that moment. No one objected, so we went in and I made my way to the book stall. I have always been attracted by books and picking up one of the new ones, I turned over its pages. As I did so, I noticed that there was no gap in the shelf from which I took it and on enquiring why this was so, I was told that what I was holding in my hand was a thought-form of the book I was interested in, the physical one on the shelf not having been moved at all. It was an amazing sensation! I wandered round the huge empty shop, for naturally at that time of evening it was closed to the public, and I heard quite plainly the clocks in a near-by department chiming the hour of six o'clock. What a lot had happened in the half-hour that had elapsed since I got out of my physical body six thousand miles away. My companions seemed highly amused at the interest I was showing in things, but Charles obviously enjoyed the unique position of guide, exactly as we all enjoy showing a friend round a new country as we so often do in the 'mysterious East' where we meet most of the big incoming liners bringing friends from home on their first visit.

Charles said he wanted to show me some of the damage that had been done to London through the raids. He took me to various places, such as St. Pauls, where it was very obvious what Londoners had suffered from these dreadful bombings. It was necessary to travel above the main buildings of the city to see the damage properly, but in our astral bodies that proved no difficulty at all. As we were walking along a street, Charles said: 'Come on,' and immediately floated over the heads of the stream of traffic. I found it quite easy to follow, as immediately I expressed in thought a wish to do the same, I found myself side by side with Charles floating gracefully and easily over the crowded metropolis of London. He suggested that we have a look at our old home in Warwickshire which I had not seen for many years, and in what seemed a few seconds only, Charles had steered me to the right spot. I asked him how he knew his way about so easily, having only lived under astral plane conditions for such a relatively short time. He told me that he had made many friends on the other side who had been only too glad to put him wise to the different conditions, and besides this his training as a pilot in the RAF had taught him quite a lot about going to places as the crow flies.

Seeing the river Avon winding its way through the lovely Warwickshire countryside was pleasant, and soon we came down to earth near the spot where our former home stood. How well I knew the old place, even though, since I had seen it last, many small houses had sprung up in the immediate neighbourhood. The house still looked the same, even the two lawns in front and behind seemed much as they had been when Charles and I played on them as youngsters. I wondered who lived there now, for after my father died, it had been sold, because my mother was not left sufficient money to keep up the place, and I, the elder son, had settled in the East. I walked inside, for by this time I was beginning to realize that a closed door made no difference, and saw strange people occupying the rooms we had loved in the old days. I supposed it was very foolish, but they seemed to me to be intruders and, with different furniture around, the atmosphere of the house had quite changed.

We did not stay very long, but soon returned to London. It was certainly very thrilling to stand in the centre of Piccadilly Circus where the flower girls used to be in the days of peace, but without the figure of Eros which had been removed to avoid damage. The crowds were still there and the buses and taxis continued on their normal rounds, the only obvious difference was the number of men and women in uniform. In fact there seemed to be more people in uniform than in civilian clothes, which brought home to me that England was not only a country at war, but a country where every able-bodied man and woman was expected to take his or her part in the defence of their beloved land.

It was nearly 7 o'clock when Charles suggested that we have dinner at the Trocadero Grill. We walked into the foyer, where we found that most of the small tables round the wall were already occupied. My Indian friend then said that he would leave me in Charles' care whilst we had dinner as he had other work to do, and he would join us later. Assuring me that Charles was well able to introduce me to this type of amusement on the astral plane, and with a cordial: 'Have a good dinner,' he left us.

Charles explained one of the very important points which must be understood when having an astral meal or drinks in a restaurant which existed in reality at the physical level, as compared with doing the same thing in a restaurant that had been created by ourselves through the medium of imagination or thought. He said that it was always unwise to sit down at a table which actually existed at the physical level, for, as we were invisible, people who came in and saw the vacant table but who did not see us, would naturally take possession of it, which would be slightly inconvenient. When they sat down they would not feel our presence but the same sort of thing would occur to us as when we passed 'through' the crowds on the streets. When a physical person sat *on* the chair that was occupied by *you* in your astral body you naturally expected to feel something, and although there was no resultant unpleasant feeling, it was not entirely pleasant. It could be avoided, he said, by producing in thought a table for one's own party in a space where, physically, no table stood. He did so right away, in the foyer of the Trocadero, and asked me to sit down.

He told me that, by thought also, he would produce a waiter who would appear to *us* exactly the same as the other waiters we saw moving about on their normal business, but that this waiter would not be seen by the physical occupants of the foyer. He did this, and at once I saw a waiter approaching our table who asked us what we would drink, in just the same way that we would have expected had we been there as ordinary members of the physical world. Charles ordered a dry sherry and I a whisky and soda, for Charles told me that my having been prohibited alcohol for the two days prior to this experiment did not apply here. I was supplied with my drink and Charles with his, and the taste to me was exactly what I had expected it to be. I was told that, had I never tasted whisky in the world, I would not have been able to appreciate the taste of it at the astral level, though I should undoubtedly have tasted in the astral liquid what I presumed to be the taste of whisky. Charles told me that one day when my Indian friend was instructing him in these things, he asked him to have a drink. He ordered a glass of water, telling Charles that it would be useless for him to order whisky, sherry or vodka as he had never tasted them in his present physical life, so not being able to imagine the taste of these drinks, all the pleasure would be lost. The same thing applies to smoking. My Indian friend never smoked, so even if offered a cigarette at the astral level he always refused it as, not knowing the pleasure derived from a cigarette, he would not have enjoyed making a thought-form of drawing in smoke and blowing it out again. That sounded quite logical and I felt glad that I had the experience of drinking and smoking, for I enjoy both of these simple pleasures.

We sipped our drinks and watched the people. We could even hear the buzz of conversation all around us and this bore out the point which had been made, that every physical sound has its astral counterpart and, as it were, sounds a note which can be heard by those using the astral body. Looking at the various types of people who were constantly coming and going, I should not have realized that at that moment England was fighting with her back to the wall, for her very existence. They all seemed to be enjoying life, and there was plenty of laughter intermingled with the chatter which continued without a break.

Charles called out to a young man dressed in air-force uniform who had just arrived; they greeted each other with much enthusiasm. Charles brought him over to our table and introduced him as Roy Chapman, a pilot who had been killed in the battle of Britain the previous autumn. He was a good type, and when I asked him how he liked living under astral world conditions, his reply was enlightening: 'It's all right,' he said, 'but boring after a time. At first of course it's rather nice being able to get everything you want without paying for it, but the novelty wears off and, frankly, I would far rather still be with the old squadron.' I thought it a unique opportunity for finding out things, so I asked him what he did with his time. He replied that he did more or less what the spirit moved him to do, and went on to say that, at the moment, he was waiting for a girl he knew, to meet him for dinner. I asked him if the girl was dead or alive. He said: 'Oh dead of course; if you still want to use that old fashioned expression. It's useless making dates with people still living in the world, as just when you are in the middle of something interesting, they have to go back to their bodies.'

In the few minutes that were left before his girl friend arrived, I gathered from him that he had tried all the usual games and found them pretty boring. To play golf for example (and he had been a low handicap man before he was killed) was pretty futile, when all you had to do was to imagine that you had a birdie or an eagle for the thing to be an established fact. There was no such thing as competition, as you only had to make a thought-form of beating your opponent for it to happen. The same applied to billiards. There was no fun in making a big break when you could always do it at will. The element of chance was lacking, which took away the charm from all games of skill. I saw that, and realized that my Indian friend was indeed right when he said that life on the astral plane could be boring for those whose interests were entirely dependent on physical plane conditions. I asked Roy whether he had been fond of music or art during his lifetime, to which he replied that he had not. He had done a spot of dancing, and liked music now and then, but he could not say that he had ever given it much serious thought. I supposed that when eventually he got tired of meeting friends and living on the fringe of the physical plane life he would find something else to interest him, or life would in time become boring in the extreme. His girl friend arrived about this time and he certainly knew how to pick them. She was beautiful, really beautiful, and they made a perfect couple as they wandered down the stairs towards the Grill Room, where presumably they had arranged to have dinner. I told Charles that I would have loved to ask him what his impressions had been when he was first thrown into astral conditions. Charles replied that he did not think he would have wanted to talk about that very much. 'None of us does, you know.' I wondered why, but I did not like to ask just then.

We then went down into the Grill Room and choosing a spot near a corner where there was no table, Charles made a thought-form of one for us. A waiter arrived almost as we sat down and asked us what we would eat. Charles told me to order anything I fancied; I must say I was not exactly hungry, but the unique experience made me order a Sole à la Bonne Femme, Chicken Maryland to follow, then a Pêche Melba and a cup of black coffee. Charles ordered two Bristol

Cream sherries and a bottle of Chambertin 1933, this being a year which he said he knew was good. I asked if these drinks were actually on the wine list in war-time, to which Charles replied that he did not know, but that in any case it didn't matter, for on the astral plane you got whatever you ordered whether it was procurable at the physical level or not. I enjoyed my dinner, the cooking being, of course as perfect as I had imagined it would be. I just could not get over my sitting (seemingly) in the Trocadero, having a perfectly normal dinner with old Charles, surrounded by just the types of people I knew would be there on almost any night of the week.

Just then I caught sight of an old pal whom I had not seen for years. The last time we met was on board ship in 1935 when I was returning to Ceylon from my home leave, and he to Malaya. I strolled over to him, leaving Charles at our table. My friend, in a party of four, was obviously enjoying himself, since he was holding forth in the way that he always did. I tapped him on the shoulder and said: 'What on earth are you doing here?' but he took no notice of me at all and continued with his story – and he certainly was in good form for I could hear every word he said and his companions were in fits of laughter. I found it quite impossible to make any impression on him so in disgust I turned back to my table, where I found Charles highly amused at my discomfort. 'How the devil could I tell whether he was real or unreal?' I asked. Charles replied that he was amused at my use of the words 'real' and 'unreal' for they just do not exist here. He explained that at first it was difficult to tell, but there was a difference: the astral body which we saw was not clearly outlined in the case of a man using his physical body, whereas that of a permanent resident in the astral world also of a man functioning at the astral level during sleep, had a much clearer outline. There was another difference to be noted and that was the faint silken cord of etheric matter which was always attached to those who were temporary visitors, who never seemed to be quite as much alive as the permanent inhabitants; you soon got used to judging, apart from the silken cord which was not easy to see. He asked me to compare Roy Chapman with the other diners in the Grill Room. There certainly was a difference, for the outline of Roy's body *was* more clearly defined than that of the others. The reason for this may be that when the astral body is being used as a permanent vehicle, the ego inhabiting it has no dual existence, as it has when the man is still living at the physical level.

Our dinner came to an end and, as I sipped my liqueur brandy, I saw that a cabaret turn was about to begin. I realized the importance of people living under the strain of total war being taken out of themselves, when possible. There certainly did not seem to be any sign of war in the scene round about us, but one could see the strain behind the apparent enjoyment of the moment, for those present all realized that the future was terribly insecure and that anything might happen to them or their loved ones at any moment. The cabaret included a sort of dance by some very lightly-clothed damsels, and during the dance they made use of every bit of space that existed between the tables of the diners. That took in the place where our astral table was situated, and again I experienced the strange sensation caused by individuals in their physical bodies passing through one's astral body.

After the cabaret Charles suggested taking me to a little night club of which he had been a member before he was shot down. I do not even remember in what street the club was situated, but I know it was between Leicester Square and Soho. The same procedure was adopted there as at the Trocadero; a table was created by Charles for our comfort, and drinks were ordered from a waiter, who presumably was also created by the imagination of my brother.

It must have been about ten o'clock by English time when the atmosphere changed without warning. The night club was crowded; there were members of the forces and a fair sprinkling of civilians also. Suddenly the sirens, denoting a raid of enemy aircraft, sounded. It was an interesting experience to see the ordered way in which everyone moved and the entire lack of panic which prevailed as all the occupants of the club hurried to the shelters situated in all sorts of strange places, apart from the tubes which played such an important part in the safety of the Londoner during air raids. We went out of the club and walked down Piccadilly. By that time it was dark, but to us the light was the same blue-grey light as when we started from Ceylon. Already we could hear the bombs dropping, also the 'ack-ack' guns that seemed to rend the air each moment. Then there was a lull and one heard the roar of fighter aircraft of one of the home squadrons going into action.

It was about this time that I found my Indian friend was with us again. He suggested that we went to see if we could help. I did not know then what he meant, but I followed all the same; we immediately soared above the buildings and found ourselves hovering above London, with enemy bombers and British fighters all round us. I noticed that Charles was no longer with us and mentioned this, wondering if he had missed us in any way. I was told that he always disappeared when 'dogfights' were taking place, as the memory of his being shot down a short time ago was still too vivid in his mind. 'We will probably see him later,' my Indian friend told me, but as a matter of fact I did not see him afterwards, although it is only now that I realize this.

We glided about amidst the inferno that was raging, the bombs and machine-guns being audible the whole time. For the first time I saw what the life of a fighter pilot actually was, and realized that some of the irresponsible actions indulged in by them between their jobs in the air were only the natural results of the strain at which they were forced to live whilst on duty. I could now very well understand why they felt that the old saying of 'Eat, drink and be merry, for tomorrow we die' referred very definitely to them, and who can blame them if they sought relaxation in every form, during the brief periods they were at liberty to enjoy themselves? My Indian friend tailed onto a particular fighter which seemed to be in the thick of the fight taking place at the moment, as if he knew what was going to happen, and within a few seconds a sudden burst of machine-gun fire sent this machine hurtling to the ground. We followed at the same speed as the 'plane which was twisting and turning on its way to earth and I saw flames appearing from the engine, which gradually enveloped the whole aircraft. With a sickening crash the 'plane reached the ground and the pilot was thrown from his cockpit amidst the wreckage. For a few moments it was a veritable inferno and although ambulances arrived almost at once, it was obvious that nothing could be done for the unfortunate pilot.

'Now you will see how those who have knowledge can help,' said my Indian friend, and as we came to rest on the ground we saw that, although the body of the airman was terribly burnt and hardly recognizable as a human being, the real man in his astral body (presumably) was standing by the body on the ground, looking frightened and intensely miserable. When my guide went up and spoke to him, he did not seem to hear or take any notice. I saw what looked like a cloak of dense matter attempting to wind itself round the astral form that was standing before us. It appeared rather like a thick elastic material and almost completely surrounded the clear-cut astral form – this winding process took only a few seconds to complete. It seemed as if what I can only describe as a wraith, came from the physical body lying on the ground and was magnetically attracted to the man standing near by. I was told later that is exactly what it was, and the explanation given to me was that the etheric double, which is forced out of the physical body at the moment of death, winds itself round the astral body in its effort to retain some form of life, for the death of the physical body means also the death of the etheric double which is part of it.

My Indian friend then made a determined effort to get rid of the fear that had taken hold of the man, for I could hear him being told that there was nothing to be frightened of and that all would be well. The boy – for he was very young – seemed to be fascinated by the actions that were taking place all around him at the physical level. He saw the ambulance men, after putting out the remnants of the fire which had raged amongst what was left of his fighter 'plane, pick up the body that was once his and reverently carry it to the waiting ambulance. I saw the boy flinch from time to time, as bombs seemed to burst near us. He wanted to follow his body, but my friend dissuaded him, talking all the time in a soothing voice, trying to make him realize that his troubles were over. Some permanent inhabitants of the astral world who were present, and easily distinguishable from the ambulance people and those who were helping at the physical level, came up to us and asked if we needed help. My friend told them to go and see to others, as he would remain and see to our 'case'.

I did not hear every word that my friend was saying, but after some time I saw that a glimmer of understanding seemed to appear on the boy's face, whereupon the clinging matter which had partly enveloped him, started to disconnect and fall to the ground. It was explained that this was effected by the boy being told to make an effort of will to disconnect himself from it. After a little time it all dropped to the ground and seemed to evaporate into smoke and dust. Later I was told that it disintegrates very quickly, because the etheric matter of which it is formed is relatively very fine, compared with the dense part of the physical body. The boy then seemed to come to life. He sat on the ground, put his head in his hands and sobbed hysterically. My friend let him do this for a time for, as he explained, the boy's emotional or astral body had undergone a very severe strain and the normal reactions must take place. The boy seemed to think that he had in some way failed, and even then did not seem to realize that he was dead and for ever out of that hell which he had known. 'Come with me and we'll talk about this,' said my friend as he took him by the arm and, without the boy seeming to notice it, we swiftly moved from the scene; within a few seconds we were far away and in the country.

My friend took him to a lovely spot near a wood, where there was a little stream wending its way down to the great river beneath, on the bank of which we sat down in a silence that was heaven after the inferno we had recently left. My friend started to talk, thus gradually breaking down the remaining sensation of fear and horror whilst the boy listened to a very brief explanation of what had taken place. At first he would not believe that he was dead and kept on saying: 'How can I be dead, when I feel so much alive?' We then asked him where he lived and he told us. 'Come along then, we'll go and see if your father and mother are asleep yet.' The boy could not understand what all this was about, but he pointed out the house where his family lived, which was beyond Finchley, and there we found the family had just retired to bed, but as yet were not asleep. The boy did not seem to realize that strangers were walking about in his house and gazing at his parents, and my friend continued talking to him so as to distract his attention from what would otherwise have seemed very strange to him. After a time first his father and then his mother fell asleep and as they slipped out of their bodies, they seemed overjoyed at seeing their son. My friend started to tell them what had happened and tried to prepare them for the news that they would receive on the morrow. At first, naturally, they were horrified at what had happened, but when they realized that their son was in no way lost to them, and that they would be able to see and contact him whenever they were asleep and out of their bodies, much of the grief which had hit them like a hammer blow, passed away.

It is a great pity that people do not remember what they have seen and been told when out of their bodies, but usually they remember nothing. I can now understand though, why so many people have a feeling before bad news is received, of an accident, or a death in the family. It is because they have been told about it on the astral plane and the following morning some slight remembrance of this has been brought back into the waking consciousness of the individual.

After spending some time with them, explaining as much as possible of what death really means, my friend suggested that the boy go with him, so that he might introduce him to a woman who was already working at the astral level and who would be only too willing to show him how to adapt himself to living under these changed conditions. We then left the boy's mother and father, who still remained seated in their astral house, talking over what they had been told. They were not a very evolved couple, so they did not wander far from their bodies, which were lying peacefully asleep on their beds, blissfully ignorant of what their owners would have to face when they woke in the morning. My Indian friend then stood quite still for a moment and uttered what sounded like a peculiar note. It was not a whistle but it was similar to that. Immediately afterwards a woman of about thirty-five years of age came up to us (out of the mist, as it were) in answer to the summons. My friend explained that to get into touch with someone at the astral level, one had to think strongly of that person and if the matter were very urgent, to help that thought, one also sounded the 'true note' of that individual. I gathered that every person has what is known as a true note, which is different from the note of anyone else, and sounding that note helped in urgent cases to bring the person needed to a particular spot in the shortest time. The person called hears the note and is magnetically drawn to the caller. The woman who answered his call was one of the many 'astral helpers', as they are called, who have dedicated themselves to the helping of those who pass from the physical world, through the process of what we call death, and I can now fully realize how necessary and wonderful is such work. Without these volunteers, not only would it take those who die much longer to get rid of that clinging etheric double – for before doing this their life at the astral level cannot properly commence – but also the advantage of having someone to instruct them in the different ruling conditions, can be easily understood. This woman was soon put into possession of all the facts of our 'case' and, with a sympathetic understanding that soon put the boy at his ease, took him away to begin his astral education. I was assured that this always happens. No one is ever left to find things out for himself, always someone is detailed to perform this necessary task; in this way a newcomer soon begins to find his feet and enters into the new life that must take the place of the old one, now behind him.

My friend then asked me what time it was and on looking at a near-by clock, I saw that the hands pointed to 2 o'clock. This meant that four hours had elapsed since the air-raid sirens had sounded, therefore it must be 6.30 a.m. in Ceylon. He said that we had only a little over one hour left as I should have to get back into my body again at 8 o'clock in Colombo. He suggested that he should introduce me to other ways of life that can be lived at the astral level by those who are not bound by the desire for things which have only a physical background. He therefore told me to keep near him and started off again. We floated over the sea with no land in sight anywhere. He asked me if I had ever been interested in knowing what was under the water and I admitted frankly that I had never thought much about it. My guide then said that at the astral level one could come into contact with entities which belonged to a parallel evolution; that fish and birds, for example, did not progress through the human kingdom on their journey to perfection, but travelled along another and quite different line, the deva or angel evolution. Before reaching the standard represented by a deva however, they had to evolve through many stages comprising elementals, nature-spirits and the like, and that if I wanted to understand something of this evolution, I had better start at the bottom and get to know them in their right sequence.

He proposed to take me under the water and warned me that whatever happened, I must not become frightened, otherwise it would mean that I would at once return to my physical body and remember nothing of what I had seen and done during the night. He reiterated the necessity of getting rid of fear in all things connected with life outside the physical conditions, and asked me if I felt I could face up to things. I have always been the type of individual who likes to try out everything once, so I expressed my willingness to go with him. I was told to realize that going below the water could not in any way affect me in my astral body, for that body did not need to breathe, so whether one were above or below water mattered not at all.

We came down on the water and although the sea appeared to be quite rough on the surface, it made no difference to us. The feel of water was little different from that of land. There was no suggestion of variation in temperature and as we gradually submerged, doing it very slowly so as to ensure my not becoming nervous, I felt no disagreeable sensation at all. As my head went below the waves, I was glad to note that the light did not change. It was still the same blue-grey light to which I was becoming accustomed. All round me were moving creatures which I recognized as fish, though not in the quantities I should have expected. As we went lower, the number of fish became less, and those I saw were considerably larger and moved much more slowly than those on the surface. There were also great hulks of what looked like floating rocks, but on coming closer I saw that they had phosphorescent eyes, betokening life of some sort. My guide explained that these entities were indeed alive, that they were at the stage of passing from the fish kingdom to that of the elemental, that such things never contacted the surface, nor did they ever see human beings, as they existed at depths far below where they could be caught in the nets of fishermen.

After a very short time, as we understand time, we reached the bottom of the sea, where we trod solid earth again; not that it seemed like earth for it was rocky and undulating. But what a sight met my eyes! The whole of the sea bottom was a garden; there were flowering shrubs, sea flowers of many kinds and rocks that glistened with a thousand different colours. Here and there I saw caves, which were not dark, but certainly less light than outside and into one of them I was taken. It was the home of one of the sea-elementals that abound at the bottom of the ocean. At first I shrank from looking at this entity, which was the size of a half-grown elephant and whose eyes shone in the gloom of the cave with a phosphorescent light that seemed to be almost magnetic. I was told that these creatures did indeed lure their food to them in the shape of sea animals and fish, by the magnetism in their eyes – I felt the magnetic draw and for a moment became a little afraid, but my Indian friend, who was never far from me, assured me that it could not harm me and that I need have no fear. The creature we were looking at was obviously aware of our presence; I was told that what we saw was its astral body.

We went out of the cave and, as I was once again drinking my fill of the beauties that surrounded me, I heard a dull, throbbing noise which seemed, in a way, to resemble music. We stood still as it came closer and soon I saw a company of about twenty strange creatures, neither fish, animal nor human. They had the heads of human beings, in that their features resembled humans, but their bodies were entirely wrapped in what looked like floating seaweed though much more beautiful than anything I had ever seen before. As they floated along just above the bottom of the ocean, they sang a song, while some played a weird pipe instrument which emitted a wailing sound reminiscent of the wind. The result was very beautiful and I was told that they were some of the sea spirits, who inhabit all deep waters. I could have listened to their music for a very long time, for it had a sort of refrain which kept on coming and going, the notes being indistinct as individual notes, but more or less blended together into a harmonious whole. It was indeed a sea symphony of which I wanted to hear more. I was told that I could easily do so another time if I wished, but that it was now time for us to be on our way.

I kept close to my guide; we soon emerged on to the surface of the sea and, without any effort whatsoever, rose into the air and continued our journey. Once more we travelled at what must have been a terrific pace, judged by earthly standards, although there was actually no feeling of speed, for within a minute we seemed to slow down and I saw we were over Colombo harbour; a moment later we were floating through the bedroom window in my bungalow which I had left less than ten hours ago.

There sure enough was my body apparently still asleep on the bed but even as we stood looking at it, I noticed that it moved and turned from one side on to its back. My guide pointed this out to me and explained that, subconsciously, it was beginning to realize that the time had nearly arrived for it to wake up again, that within a few minutes an SOS would be sent out and, even if I were ten thousand miles away, I should have to return immediately, as this summons meant that the physical body had had its proper quota of sleep and wished to take up its work in the world again.

I asked how it was possible to ensure that the body would always remain asleep for a specified number of hours. He replied that it was difficult to ensure this, but that with much training and concentration it was possible so to discipline the body that it acted according to one's will, but this I gathered took much time and training to do properly. I asked if the tablet I had taken before going to bed the previous night had had anything to do with it, and was told that in this case it had. The tablet was a special kind of sleeping draught made from a secret formula which not only ensured the person going to sleep almost immediately, but also made certain that the body remained asleep for a period of ten hours, unless awakened by some extraordinary amount of noise or on being touched by an outside agency. It was impressed upon me that if I wished to experiment with such matters as bringing back into the physical consciousness what I had been doing whilst out of my body, it was essential that I trained my domestic staff never to wake me or make any noise near my bedroom during the period that I wished to remain asleep.

My Indian friend then told me that it was time for me to return to my body and that he would endeavour to impress upon the brain cells of that body the necessity for remembering what had transpired during the night, so that there should be no actual break of consciousness at the moment of awakening. He told me to set to, as soon as I was conscious in my physical body, and make notes of what I had done during the night and that immediately I had bathed and eaten, I should waste no time in writing down in detail all that I remembered.

Almost as soon as my guide had finished speaking, I felt myself gradually sliding *into* my body again and I woke without having any break of consciousness, as he had hoped. I sat up in bed, drew towards me a pad and pencil that I had placed beside my bed and started to make notes of all that had happened during the night. It was fortunate that I was told to make notes immediately, for I found that even with the headings that I had made, it was difficult to remember exactly what had happened, when, later on, I wrote out my report in full. However, I shall see how faithful my memory has been when I show this record to my visitor tomorrow, for he said he would come then to continue his talks.

CHAPTER FIVE

It was no use; last night I made all my preparations and concentrated on seeing myself in a mirror, but this morning I remember absolutely nothing. I went to sleep almost as soon as my head touched the pillow, for I suppose I was tired after all the concentration on my report yesterday, and it seemed only a very short time before I awoke this morning, bright and early, after a dreamless night's rest. Yes, not even a dream disturbed my slumbers and I must say I am disappointed, though possibly I was expecting too much. In an hour's time my Indian friend will be here and perhaps he will explain why I failed last night in such a dismal fashion.

Just at 11 o'clock, as I was looking through my notes uncertain as to what he would think about them, he opened the door. Obviously he knew that I was a little excited, wondering whether I had failed to remember a lot about my astral journey, for his eyes twinkled as he asked me if my report was ready. He never seems to laugh, though his eyes often smile, and there is no doubt at all about his having a very highly developed sense of humour.

Having read my notes, he complimented me on having remembered so much and said that for a first attempt it was distinctly above the average. I asked him if I had forgotten much, to which he replied that I had certainly failed to notice quite a lot when we were under the sea, also I had not remembered much of what transpired when we were trying to help the young fighter-pilot immediately after he had been shot down; these omissions were unimportant, the main thing being that I had proved for myself it is possible to remember what is done outside the body, and the perfecting of the 'bringing through' process of the business was now only a matter of time and concentration.

'But why couldn't I remember anything this morning?'

He smiled as he pointed out that I must not expect to be successful all at once, and that I must be prepared for many disappointments, yet if I were really determined to succeed, he would help me in every way possible. He continued: 'Your adventures of the night before last have made my task of describing the astral plane to you much easier than it was before, for now you know from experience something of what I have endeavoured to explain to you in mere words. You have therefore learnt the first lesson in what we call occult wisdom, which is that you must never believe in a credulous way anything that you are told. You must not disbelieve it either, for that would be foolish. The only method to adopt is to accept as a possibility the things that you are told, then to set about finding out the way to prove those things for yourself.

'Now what have we *proved* so far? That is where I wish to begin. You have proved that it is possible to have experiences apart from your physical body. You have proved that death is not what you thought it was, for you have seen your brother Charles and you know that he is very much alive indeed though invisible to you whilst you are functioning in your physical body; you have talked to him, and this should be sufficient proof that he exists in a region where you can follow him at stated times. You are aware that although Charles still knows very little of astral plane conditions, you could not honestly say he was suffering, nor that his life was a miserable one and something from which a man would naturally shrink. You therefore have taken one step towards getting rid of the fear of death, the fear which makes such a deep impression on so many men living in the world. Even from your present knowledge you know that death is not the tragedy it is so often called and that in some cases it might easily be considered not only a relief, but a great blessing. You have seen for yourself that existence after death is to a great extent governed by the type of life lived in the world – you can appreciate that those who are artistically inclined or interested in one or other of the specific branches of art such as music, painting, literature or philosophy, or even those whose special interest is travel, are well catered for after death. On the other hand you can also appreciate that those whose lives here are purely material, whose amusements and interests depend on the physical body, who primarily are drawn to sport, to good living, to forms of business which have as their goal the making of money are going to find time hanging heavily on their hands after death, until they realize that they can develop new interests.

I asked 'How can one develop new interests after death?'

'In the same way as you could have developed them during your lifetime, had you possessed sufficient leisure and the money to provide fees for the necessary tuition. At the astral level, although you have not yet seen them for yourself, schools exist, because of the great need of training permanent inhabitants of the world in those interests which they lack, for the life that is before them. These schools serve a dual purpose; they not only teach pupils all about conditions at the astral level and how best they can employ the conditions ruling there for their pleasure and education, but also provide courses of instruction in all the various matters for which physical plane conditions are not essential for carrying them out.

'Most of the true musicians, artists, philosophers and those who were teachers or professors in the physical world, obtain great joy from passing on some of their knowledge and experience to those who are lacking in it but who are sufficiently interested to want to learn. The absence of the time factor – the absence of the necessity to sleep eight hours out of the twenty four – again helps considerably. If experts in their particular subjects give even as little as three or four hours a day to training new students, the time given is in no way a hardship, for they still have the remaining twenty hours out of each day for their own devices. In actual practice, it works out that many of these ex-teachers and specialists in their particular arts obtain so much pleasure from moulding new material into form, that they attach themselves quite voluntarily to these schools and often spend more than half their time at the astral level teaching others the rudiments of their arts, or in some cases helping those who have already developed some proficiency to become adepts under the concentrated tuition that is available in the astral world.

'Not only do these schools play a tremendous part in the life of the astral world, but they undoubtedly influence the future lives of their pupils. If, at the astral level, a man has developed a love of any of the arts or sciences, in his next life at the physical level he is born with the *desire* to continue that study and so we find children showing at an early age an enthusiastic aptitude for one thing or another, which perhaps is not in any way a characteristic of their parents. Such leanings towards an art should always be encouraged. Parents often argue that this enthusiasm should be discouraged, as they themselves have managed to lead successful lives without such dabbling. This is a great mistake, however, and if the parents perceived that the craving of the child is a perfectly natural one, that it is really only anxious to carry on with the training which was begun during its last astral care-free life, they would probably realize that such cravings should be encouraged and not squashed, as so often they are. Both in this world and the next we are all the time progressing and making our future lives happier and fuller.

'The permanent inhabitants find out these schools in different ways and always at a stage when they are of most use. When they first realize that they are living in the astral world, it is quite useless to mention such things to them, for they will at once assure you that they have no desire to go to school again. They want to enjoy themselves. For the first few months the opportunity of travelling round the world and seeing all the countries they had not had the chance of visiting whilst they were in this world usually satisfies them.

'You will remember that Roy Chapman, your brother's friend, admitted that at times he felt bored. He had done all these things; he had made a few friends of course and enjoyed taking them out to dinners and shows, to picnics and the like, but that palls after a time. Roy was a keen golfer in his lifetime, but golf is not the interesting game in the astral world that it is here. Such a man as Roy will certainly tire of all the things that he has been doing for the last six months or so, and when he does, he will not hesitate to express his boredom to others whom he meets in that world. Then one day someone to whom he has been introduced will mention to him the opportunities that exist there for increasing one's knowledge or developing along a particular line of art or study. He will not be enthusiastic at first, but he soon will realize that learning something entirely new will fill in the long hours; eventually his interest will be aroused, and yet another will have passed from the stage of materialist to the life that makes our sojourn at the astral level all too short.

'There are others to whom these new interests have no appeal. They are usually the old married couples, who have developed a taste for domestic life. All they have ever aspired to was to have a home, a garden and to live a quiet life amongst their friends. They liked to listen to the radio, have a television set and such things. Their happiness is dependent upon being together. They can carry on this type of life at the astral level, without any difficulty whatever. If the man dies first, he wanders round looking miserable and lonely at the hours when his wife is awake, and is there to meet her as soon as she gets out of her body at the time when she falls asleep. To suggest to such a man that there are schools where he can learn something is usually a waste of time; he scorns the idea, all he wants is a comfortable home with his partner. He sets to, to find out the ways and means of living in such a way as he and his wife will enjoy when reunited. He learns that it is simplicity itself to have a house and garden exactly in accordance with his own pet ideas merely by expressing a desire for such, in thought. He finds the most beautiful spot available, and when his wife comes over they build their dream house and furnish it exactly as they would have loved to do in the world had they had the necessary means to do so. Now a thought produces just the things they desire, and frequently they think of wonderful labour saving appliances. Sometimes these are seen by businessmen who make notes of them, and in their next life they invent similar things. This old couple has an ultra-modern stereo set and they create in thought the required number of servants to do their bidding. They create a garden with any form of flower or fruit in it that they would like – for here there is no limitation of climate. They entertain their friends, they enjoy showing off their inventions and live very happily in the astral plane. Frequently they link up with pets they have had on earth, or adopt others.

'The blissful state of the elderly couple just described is not as general as might be supposed. Men and women marry for various reasons; sometimes it is physical attraction which draws them together, sometimes wealth; even loneliness plays its part in the linking up of individuals. It is very seldom that we see what we would describe as an ideal pair – two people whose outlook on life dovetails, whose standing in evolution is similar, each having sufficient intelligence to be able to enter into the problems of the other. Such unions are rare and, occultly, are not to be greatly desired as it is a good thing for an evolved man to be attracted in some particular way to a less evolved partner.

'When one hears such a remark as: "What a pity John married Mary, so unsuited, don't you think?" one must realize that if the speaker had more experience he would know that both these two young people are destined to benefit considerably from the few years they spend together. The immediate outcome of such an apparently unsuitable union is invariably a series of difficulties for both parties; there is always a clash of interests. Possibly the man was originally drawn to the woman through her physical attractions. After a time that "draw" becomes less (though it is unlikely that it would cease to function altogether) then the two people are thrown back on companionship as the only bond to hold them together; but companionship is not easy when the tastes and desires of two individuals are dissimilar. In the case where the man is the more evolved of the two, his interests lie in books, in music, in the serious side of life, whereas the woman wants to go to any place of amusement where her friends of the moment are going. A clash of ideas results and there are many arguments and disagreements. If there are no children sometimes the marriage breaks up, solely on account of the incompatibility of temperaments, but it is a great pity when this happens because it is through the inequality of the two people concerned that much knowledge and experience can be gained. The man has to learn a method of meeting his partner half way. When he ponders over ways and means of doing this, he realizes that he must start by raising his wife's interests towards his educational level – at the same time making sure that she does not realize what he is endeavouring to do, or she will immediately develop an inferiority complex. He must learn to be patient when, through her inexperience she presses for things he knows to be unwise or unnecessary. Knowing that to do so is wrong, sometimes he must give way in order that she may see the results of the mistake which has been made. The woman will not always wish to be led, even when subconsciously she realizes that her partner in life is wiser than she. If two such people *can* spend a lifetime together, the benefits to both are great indeed, for one will have had the advantage of a superior intelligence and a greater experience to guide her and develop her character, whereas the other has had to learn the value of patience, of tact, of the necessity to see things from another's point of view, a view which through lack of experience must be more limited than his own.

'After death such people do not necessarily carry on their lives together; the man probably feels that he wishes to spend his time with greater minds than his own, whereas the woman, who for many earthly years has been forced to live at high pressure endeavouring to produce a standard which was always something of an effort for her, now wishes to sit back and take things easy for a time. Usually, after a short period of relative inactivity, she finds that the seeds sown during her lifetime have now brought forth a strong desire to continue the development already begun. She finds that she no longer derives complete satisfaction from the artificial enjoyments she once longed for and bullied her unresponsive husband to provide for her. Her mental appetite has been whetted and she finds it is impossible for her to go back to the standards which were natural to her at the time of her marriage on the physical plane. She will tell you that she did not have a particularly happy life but, now that it is over, she will be glad that Fate decreed that the experience should have been hers.

'It often happens that two people who have lived together for a whole lifetime do not contact each other again, either after death or in future lives. Each has served the other, both have benefited by being brought together for a period of time, but their outlook on life is too different for either to be naturally attracted to the other. In such an instance it is possible that the man had lived at least fifty to a hundred lives more than the woman; naturally his understanding of the vast "plan" would be greater than hers, his reservoir of knowledge (that accumulation of experience from past lives) would be greater than hers and in every way he could be regarded as a superior being. But do not forget that a hundred lives previous to this one he was in the same place as his wife of the moment, and he probably benefited from having been forced to spend a lifetime with someone much more highly developed than himself.

'You have probably heard it said that every person has what is known as a soul-mate and that you should always be on the lookout for such a person. It is quite true that soul-mates exist, for originally when the life force is sent out by Divine Power, the force emerges into life as twin forms, one male, one female. Both these forms evolve quite separately, each having its quota of lives in male and female bodies, but on special occasions, when a great work has to be done, these two entities are sometimes brought together, because the inspiration of the one enables the other to carry out the gigantic task which has to be accomplished. A great man who has achieved his goal has often said that he could never have done it without the help, the advice and the strengthening power of his wife. This need not mean that they were soul-mates, but it may mean just that, and when this is so the two people seem to act as one great unit, they not only think the same thoughts but they feel instinctively what is right for both of them. It is of course the perfect blending of the positive and negative, of the male and female in nature. It would not be a good thing for us always to have lives with our soul-mates, for under such circumstances we should tend to grow very selfish; we would never learn to see things from others' points of view; to deal with opposite ideas; to give way in order to achieve something rather than to stand firm and produce nothing.

'These illustrations give you some small idea of the way in which egos are assisted along their evolutionary journey. It is through difficulties such as having to live with individuals who do not synchronize in every way that we learn true tolerance. A pleasant and peaceful life is not necessarily the best life, we progress most quickly along the evolutionary path through suffering and what often seem hard and ruthless methods. Each life is a day in the school of evolution and, if we are to carry out the purpose for which we were sent into incarnation, we cannot afford to waste any opportunities.

'Tomorrow I shall tell you a few facts about the non-human inhabitants of the astral plane, after which I shall take you for another astral journey so that you may see for yourself that astral human beings conform to what may be described as the normal reactions covering the individual concerned in the physical plane.'

CHAPTER SIX

The prospect of being taken on another astral journey by my Indian teacher has made me quite excited, and thinking about what may happen has taken away some of the disappointment I feel in not yet having achieved any results when alone. Last night I concentrated on seeing myself lying on my bed, as I certainly did the night I was helped. When I woke this morning I felt well rested, I remembered it had taken me a long time to go to sleep, but of what had happened to me after I lost consciousness, I could recall absolutely nothing. I *must* find out how this business of bringing things through can be accomplished. I know it is no use worrying about not being able to learn the tricks of the trade at once, for worrying more often hinders than helps. I suppose the only thing I *can* do is to persevere with this concentration which I am told is so important a part of the proceedings, until I make some small beginning from which to work.

'It is useless feeling disappointed.' My Indian friend was standing behind me where I was writing; I had not heard him open the door. 'That is what happens in so many instances. People are shown a glimpse of the truth and because they cannot at once do the things that they know are possible for others, they get discouraged and give up trying. Often people say: "Obviously this occult life is not for me", whereas all that is necessary to achieve results is a little patience and the determination to break through the wall which separates our worldly existence from the life we lead when asleep. Do not expect too much, my friend. Remember it is less than two weeks since you sat here bowed in grief, not even knowing for certain that death was the logical sequence of life. Now at least you know something, and soon you will be given the opportunity of knowing more.

'You are thinking: "Why do not more people know these things?" Perhaps they have not asked for knowledge, for help, as you asked; perhaps they are quite satisfied with one of the many orthodox religions, which tell them to have faith and to believe that everything sent is the will of God. All happenings are certainly the will of God, but it is easier if we realize why such things are. It is easier if there is a logical answer to every question, also if it is made possible for each individual who takes the trouble, to prove things for himself, thereby making the acceptance of statements made on a basis of faith unnecessary. Faith is always good, but knowledge is better. You must have faith whilst acquiring knowledge and whatever happens, you must never lose heart. Evolution is a slow process and can seldom be hurried, though the activities of an individual can be inspired by encouragement and by help given at the right moment.

'So far you have seen only a tiny sector of the astral world, the sector usually occupied by those who have recently passed from this world through the portal known as death. Once you have established yourself as an inhabitant of the astral world, you seldom visit such places, but you can go if you wish. You do from time to time, for example when you meet special friends and relations who die and so require some help from the regular inhabitants, in exactly the same way that you require help from friends living in a foreign country which you are visiting as a tourist or as a new settler.

'The astral world is divided into what are known as spheres, levels or sub-planes. It is necessary to know that such spheres exist or you will never be able to understand how the machinery of this world operates. Most teachers illustrate their point by asking their students to understand the densest sphere of the astral world as being the conditions which exist whilst standing on the ground. In this sphere there is a counterpart of everything that exists in the physical world; where there is a town or a building in the physical world, there also, in the astral matter, is the counterpart or reflection of that town or building, which you can see quite clearly when you function at the astral level in your astral body. Imagine the astral counterpart of Piccadilly Circus, London, which you visited a few nights ago, as representing the noisy lowest sphere. Then imagine a similar world, say one mile above the lowest world, to which one can transport oneself in a second's time by an effort of will; this corresponds to the second sphere of the astral world, less dense than the first sphere, but still rather materialistic and akin to physical plane conditions. If you were existing one mile above London, you might still hear something of the roar of London's traffic and the noise that is always part of the life of a great city, but that would be only a murmur compared with the noise you hear standing on the ground floor, as it were. Now imagine a third sphere of consciousness yet another mile above the second sphere and you can visualize the probability that when you are living in the third sphere of the astral world you would be so far removed from the noise and bustle of London town, that you would not only be unaffected by its existence, but would be more or less unconscious of it.

'There are seven spheres of consciousness in the astral world, each less material than the one "below" it, and permanent inhabitants can spend their astral lives on any of these spheres, according to their natural desires. For example, a man may spend a few weeks on the first sphere, then the next two years on the second sphere, later passing to the third or fourth, as his habits and desires become less material and more artistic, intellectual or spiritual. Thus there is never any possibility of overcrowding in this world.

'In this physical world a man's choice of where he will live is limited. On account of his work, through which he earns the money necessary for existing here, he may be forced to live in places which he would not otherwise choose. Many parts are uninhabitable owing to climate or other difficulties. A man cannot exist comfortably at either the North or the South Pole owing to extreme cold and other limitations such as lack of sunshine and daylight at certain times of the year; he cannot live in many of the existing deserts, owing to lack of water; he cannot live in the dense jungles, for here there are wild beasts which must first be exterminated before it is safe to build a house to live in. In the astral world he does not encounter these limitations. The climate is the same at the North or South Poles as anywhere else on the astral plane, there is nowhere any limitation of daylight as the light is everywhere the same for twenty four hours of every day; in the desert he does not need water for his existence; if he wishes to live in the astral counterparts of the jungles, he can – there are no wild beasts to attack him for just as a man learns he cannot harm an animal in the astral world so the animals learn that they cannot harm man. In addition there are seven spheres of consciousness to choose from, so it is always possible to obtain the conditions required to make practicable the type of life desired, amidst surroundings which are in accordance with a man's emotional, mental and spiritual development. Once you get a grasp of these different types of existence which make up the life which follows this one here, it will be easy for you to see how all parts of the jig-saw puzzle fall perfectly into their places, and the Evolutionary Path becomes a logical sequence of events controlled by natural laws, sound in theory as well as in practice.

'All these facts are explained and taught in the schools which exist on some of the astral spheres and it is usually through these schools, which a man hears about in one way or another at the appropriate time, that the urge or desire to pass from one sphere to another is born. In these schools the astral entity is shown the way in which to transport himself from one level to another – the change being brought about through an effort of will made in a particular way; for although the matter of which an individual sphere is composed is different from the matter of which the other spheres are composed, our astral bodies include matter similar to that of all the spheres and it is only a question of making active the atoms in our bodies relative to the sphere concerned, to enable us to function fully in the sphere chosen. A further point which the astral entity is taught is that a man functioning on the second sphere cannot contact or communicate with one functioning on the first sphere – nor a man on the third with one on the second. If a man living at the third level wishes for any reason to get into touch with a person living on the first level, he must again descend to the first level by an action of will, which, as I said, makes the first sphere atoms in his body become active again. The same process is applied when going "up" or "down". The life expressed at the different spheres is separate and to all intents and purposes self-contained, in exactly the same way that life in England is separate and different from life in India. Both countries are part of the physical world; all spheres are part of the astral world, but they work separately and for very definite reasons.

The most material part of the astral world – the densest part – is the sphere which surrounds you immediately after death, and whilst you live in this dense part of the astral world you see all the things around you that you saw when you were living in the physical world. Say you lived in London during your lifetime, it is more than probable that after death you would remain in the astral counterpart or reflection of London, merely because, to begin with, you want to remain in touch with something which you understand; you want to see people around you, and to have a perfect home where you can entertain friends as before. Then one day, perhaps a friend points out to you that life in town has few advantages in the astral world, and suggests that you see the beauties of the countryside. You can easily visualize the difference in atmosphere between an existence amongst the teeming millions which comprise a metropolis and the comparative peace of a country village, where the inhabitants are counted in dozens instead of thousands or millions. This is the second sphere which, for want of a better description, I have suggested should be thought of as being one mile above the level of the first sphere, and here you would find many families happily carrying on their existence, with social intercourse and the usual things which go with the idea of the perfect country life.

'You can live in these spheres as long as you like. A very coarse and material type of person is happiest in the densest part of the astral world, for that part is nearest to and most like the physical world to which he is so attached, and here he continues to live a very limited existence. These are not spheres in which a developed person

– a man who has some spiritual background – would be particularly happy were he forced to remain under these conditions for long. He is not so forced; and, after passing through the purgatory period in which he is shown the results of the good and evil actions of this past life, the realization of which influences his future character, he begins to feel an urge to get away from anything which is similar to the life that is over, and the revelation comes to him of the immense possibilities for interesting and profitable experiences which await him in the higher and less dense spheres of the astral world. Eventually he settles down to live his astral life surrounded by conditions which are in keeping with his actual development, this may be on the third sphere, where he meets the type of individual who is a creator – musicians, artists, scientists etc. – or on the fourth sphere, where he can discuss world problems with men who have greater intellects than himself.

'When an astral entity of human origin reaches these spheres, he becomes aware that they are also inhabited by other entities which, he finds, are of non-human origin. It is important that you know something about these entities and their origin before you have further astral experiences, so I shall tell you something about them now. These entities comprise a parallel evolution called the deva or angel kingdom. They evolve in a similar way to the human kingdom, in that instead of individualizing from the animal kingdom into the human, these entities, which previously were seen and known as insects, fish or birds, individualize into elementals, nature-spirits and devas or angels. When the time comes for a bird or fish to progress to the next stage of its development, it becomes either an elemental or a nature-spirit, according to its type in the physical world.

'You will remember when I took you under the sea on your first astral journey, I showed you some of the elementals that live at the bottom of the ocean. Originally these were fish, and in their natural journey towards their goal of perfection, they have to change from fish to elementals in just the same way that dogs, cats, horses etc., change from their animal types into the unevolved types of humans that we know of in the world. Birds for example, turn into nature-spirits – fairies they are sometimes called – and both these elementals and nature-spirits after many progressive lives, reach a stage where they become what the world describes as devas or angels.

'Now there is a great difference between the two evolutions, in that the deva evolution does not inhabit the physical world after the fish or bird has progressed to the elemental or nature-spirit stage. It only inhabits the astral and mental worlds and apart from the lower elementals and very junior or unevolved types of nature-spirits, they do not live below the third sphere of that astral world. That is why so little is known of this evolution by people living in the physical world. They hardly contact it, as far as the ordinary individual is concerned, though human beings who have developed the dormant sense of clairvoyance can of course see these creatures even at the physical level, for there is no closed door to the clairvoyant between the astral and the physical worlds of consciousness. But as I have said, the average man has no such knowledge and usually he ridicules the stories that are circulated, concerning the existence of such entities.

'It is only in undeveloped countries, where the inhabitants are nearer to nature than the average, that the "little people" as fairies and nature-spirits are called in Ireland, are recognized. There, although the majority of people have never seen them, the leprechauns, gnomes and elves are acknowledged to exist. To this day many farmers refuse to till a particular piece of land, which folk-lore maintains is used by the fairies. Many are the stories that are told, where materialistic modern owners of the land scoffing at the old stories as rubbish and superstition have suffered misfortune which the local inhabitants put down to their having insulted the little people. I do not propose to comment on whether these "bad-luck" stories are founded on fact or not, for frankly, it would be impossible to give any general opinion on the subject. Each case would have to be separately investigated, in order to ascertain the truth, and it does not happen to be my present task to make such investigations. I tell you, however, that on the astral plane these entities not only exist, but they play an important part in the life of the astral world, and after death, when you reach the third and higher spheres, you will not only see them for yourself, but will have contact with them as I shall describe.

'When a man passes to the fourth sphere he would at first be impressed by the entire absence of what might be described as activity. He would meet people there of course and, if he had not already met them in his past physical life, be introduced to them in exactly the same way as people are introduced in the physical world. He would be welcomed as a man of similar interests to themselves by the permanent inhabitants of that sphere who know that he could not have progressed as far as the fourth sphere, unless he had the necessary desire and qualifications to enable him to function there. Instead of physical activity he would find much mental activity, for the main interest of the inhabitants there is discussing international and evolutionary problems – discussions relating to the development of science, discussions relating to the parallel evolution of the deva kingdom with its great differences from our evolution and so on – or the formulating of theories, which they endeavour to test out. All this may sound very dull to you, but to an intellectual type of individual, it is not dull at all. Of course the people one meets vary intellectually and those who have the finest intellects – who are actually the older and more experienced souls – take the lead in the discussions, as is natural for them to do. In many cases, members of the deva kingdom join the deliberations, though intercommunication in such instances is not made through the medium of words, for although not yet living in the mental world – where everything is governed by thoughts – it is found that in the higher levels of the astral world conversations can be carried on without the actual use of words. Life is so much less material there that the possibilities of exchange of thoughts comes quite naturally and there is no question of such things being considered either marvellous or extraordinary.

'You must remember that the devas who inhabit the fourth sphere of the astral world are also evolved beings – as different from the low-type elementals and nature-spirits as evolved men are different from the low types of coolies met with in the physical world. The mental outlook of a deva is quite different from the mental outlook of a human; the deva is mostly interested in the processes of nature. Their lives are so mixed up with natural features – oceans, mountains, trees, flowers, rainfall and the like – that they do not seem to be the slightest bit affected by the problems of life which interest mankind, except in special cases where their assistance is desired. Although the growth or decline of nations does not touch them, the progress of plant life, the scientific research work whereby nature provides man with his physical needs, interests them greatly. There is an evolved deva in charge of each different type of tree, shrub or flower. Under these "controllers" work thousands of assistants, all of whom seem to have their special duties. Where too many trees are cut down by the inroads of so-called civilization, the deva evolution endeavours to produce new trees to take the place of those destroyed. The experiments of modern science, in such efforts as producing rain by artificial means, are matters of great interest to the deva kingdom, and in their own way they endeavour to influence man in his research activities, along the right lines.

'The deva kingdom expresses itself through colour, and anyone who is interested in landscape gardening will see marvellous results achieved by the devas in their activities on the third and fourth spheres of the astral world. In exactly the same way that a scientific gardener in the physical world endeavours to produce flowers of different colours by judicious grafting and pollination, the deva experiments also and, as his knowledge is so much greater in that he is nearer to nature than his human counterpart, produces much more beautiful results. It is quite impossible to describe in words the beauty of the flowers produced by the deva kingdom, for there are many hundreds of colours where we only have dozens, and we have no names for these minute variations of what we call reds, blues and purples.

'The devas also seem to express themselves in sound, with a view to influencing the activities of life. We often talk about "producing the right atmosphere", and what we mean by that, usually, is getting people into a harmonious frame of mind. The devas express themselves as an evolution in a much bigger way and that which is called deva music is the result. Large numbers of devas gather together in woods and dells, using weird wood instruments to produce the most beautiful sounds, always in perfect harmony. Their voices seem to be pitched much higher than human voices, but are much softer; they do not use words as we understand words. They sing mostly in huge choirs, but there are also soloists who from time to time sing by themselves, the main choir remaining silent whilst the passage is being rendered. The soloists usually perch themselves on high trees some distance from the main choir and the result is absolutely amazing to our ears. It is quite impossible to give an adequate description of these "concerts" to anyone who has not heard them, but undoubtedly they produce an atmosphere which the devas say affects the whole human race. It is probably their way of expressing peace and goodwill to all men, for they certainly could never understand the differences of opinion in the world that can lead to such things as modern wars.

'The deva has no possessions, as we understand possessions, nor does he need any. From his early days as a nature spirit he does not have to earn money in order to support himself and so, perhaps, he can be considered more fortunate than his human counterpart.

'Although these devas do not seem to laugh or enjoy themselves in ways that we understand, they are only too willing to be friendly and helpful to man when called upon. In some ways they do not seem to be interested in human affairs at all, yet in special cases, where earthquakes or volcanic eruptions have taken place, they seem to have their special work to do, for anything to do with nature, land, sea, flora or fauna, is their world. An earthquake or volcanic eruption is a natural phenomenon affecting part of the earth's surface. When these tragedies take place, large numbers of devas are sent to help where they can. What exactly they do, I cannot tell you, but they certainly have their part to play in the scheme of things and one day I expect we shall know more about their work than we do today.

'They also play their part in helping with human emotions. As I have said, bodily illness is quite unknown under astral conditions, but emotional upsets, where people become extremely depressed, occur, for the astral world is the world of emotion and the astral body is our vehicle of emotional consciousness. In such cases, the devas seem to nurse depressed people back to emotional health. They soothe the people and bring them into touch with their divine music, the effect of which on one who is not very happy is very marked indeed. It is not often that one sees a really unhappy individual in the astral world, for the conditions there make it difficult to be unhappy, but there are cases where people are troubled, and the deva people then act as doctors and nurses in a very effective way.

'I have given you sufficient to think about before I take you on your second astral journey, so I shall not visit you tomorrow but shall come again in three days' time. I am leaving another tablet with you; take it as before, when you go to bed tomorrow night – then you will certainly be asleep by 10 o'clock. I shall meet you at the moment that you go to sleep. Do not eat any meat or drink alcohol between now and then, and when you wake up in the morning, the day after tomorrow, write down immediately all that you remember. I shall help you to remember, as I did before. Today, write up your notes of this talk; tomorrow study all your notes up to date, and tomorrow evening we will journey together in our astral bodies. Expect me at 11 o'clock on the following day, when I hope you will have a full account of your experiences ready for me. I leave you now.'

What a morning! The weather was exceedingly warm and humid and my Indian friend had talked for longer than he usually does, though what he said has been even more interesting than it has been on the days that have gone before. He is opening up a new vision of life in the world that follows this, which, if true, certainly makes the contacting of that world even more interesting than it was before. Not only am I excited at the prospect of another astral journey, but if this trip turns out to be equally thrilling to the one I had last week, then it will be wonderful indeed. I do not remember having seen Charles since that memorable night and somehow I have not been in any way worried about this, for now I *know* that he is all right. The absence of his physical presence worries me no more; I am no longer sad; I feel that at any time I *can* contact him if the need is great and also there is the feeling which amounts to a certainty, that he is *not* gone from us, that he is still very much in the land of the living. What this means to me is difficult to describe in mere words, but I am already beginning to want to talk to other people who are sad for the same reason that I was sad, to comfort them and explain something of this scheme which seems to rule the Universe. Perhaps that is one of the reasons why I have been helped, for the urge to pass on this information to others, and have the capacity for giving them proof such as my Indian friend is able to give me, is very strong within me. Possibly one day I shall be able to put my urge into effect.

The next evening I went to the cinema and as it was a thriller, it held my interest for a couple of hours. I went to bed immediately I returned and tried the trick of imagining a mirror over my bed just before I settled myself for sleep. This time I did get a little result, for at the moment of losing consciousness I remember finding myself standing in my bedroom and there, sure enough, was my body lying peacefully on the bed. I remember distinctly starting to open my bedroom door; even as I put my hand on the knob, I found that I was, as it were, half through the door and immediately I remembered that doors are no obstacle to the astral body, so I wandered forth. I glided down the stairs a foot or so above the steps and I recollect this because I lowered my head so as to miss the overhang at the point where the stairs turn the corner. Of course bowing my head was quite unnecessary, but it was instinctive on my part. I went through the front door and floated gently towards the harbour and sea. The next thing I remember was waking up this morning at the usual hour. I lay quite still delving deeply into my inner consciousness, but nothing more than the few details that started off my night's rambling could I recall. Never mind, even that is something, and I am rather thrilled to find that without help I was able to retain continuity of consciousness at the moment of going to sleep and even remember the first stage of my astral journeyings.

It is 9.30 p.m.; I have finished my light dinner. I am now going to take the tablet and get into bed. What will I experience this time?

CHAPTER SEVEN

This time I do not seem to have been asleep at all! When I realized this morning that I was again *in* my body, the remembrance of everything that had taken place was clear in my brain – just as if I had been to a theatre and had been asked to write down all the details of the play. Thus I was able to settle down with my pad and pencil and record faithfully everything that had happened.

After taking the tablet, I looked at my little French clock whose hands stood at 9.42 p.m. I did not try to go to sleep, but within a few minutes I found that I had slipped out of my body and was standing at the side of the bed, with my sleeping form lying there upon it. Again I looked, and it was five minutes to ten. There was no one about and I walked round my room marvelling at the simplicity of what, on the occasion of my first astral journey, had struck me as extremely complicated. I did not attempt to leave my room for I remembered quite clearly that my Indian friend had said that he would be here at 10 o'clock, so I awaited his coming, quite sure that he would not let me down. Next time I looked at my clock, it was 10 o'clock; still nothing happened. Five minutes passed and I wondered whether the whole thing was going to turn out a flop. I became more and more worried as the minutes ticked away, but refused to be tempted to experiment on my own, and just as I was about to look at my clock again, I heard the now familiar voice behind me saying: 'Did you think I was going to disappoint you?'

My friend stated that he was late because he had been helping a particular friend of his who had died that morning. He said this man had dreaded dying and, although he had been ill for many months, he had fought death right up to the end. He explained that this was quite useless, as his time had come, and although he had probably kept life in his body for a few weeks by his extreme will-power, in the end death had prevailed. The illness this man had suffered from, for months, had at last so weakened his physical body that it was impossible for the etheric matter to remain within it. He stated that he had been helping this man to get rid of his etheric vehicle, which he tried to keep with him, this being now the nearest thing to the physical life – the only life he understood. Getting the man to make the necessary effort of will to disconnect the etheric from the astral body, round which it had wound itself, had taken longer than usual. 'He's all right now,' he said, ' and I have left him with some astral helpers, who will probably wish to remain – until through practical experience he learns something about the Law.'

I asked him what we were going to do this time; he replied that it was desirable I should first get experience of passing from the lower to the higher spheres. He took a lot of trouble in explaining to me that although he called them higher spheres, they were not actually above each other, but rather all round us, being conditions of different density only.

He suggested we should start our expedition from London, so we set off as we had done the last time, and in no time slowed down over what was obviously land; almost at once I recognized the huge city below us as London. The objects we passed on our way were in no way clear; I could just distinguish between land and sea – it was as if we were looking at a moving picture of scenery which was being projected on to a screen at a very quick rate. There was no effort whatsoever in moving and although it took us what seemed to be less than a minute, we did not arrive breathless in any way.

We dropped down as before in Hyde Park; I was told that this was the best place to land as, although we were going to Piccadilly Circus, to land there could easily cause me to get frightened owing to the terrific traffic and the possibility of my feeling (quite erroneously) that I might get run over. If I were to get frightened in this way, my fear would be transmitted to my physical body on the bed in Colombo, which would immediately endeavour to attract its owner back to it. The fear having caused me in my astral body to return hurriedly to my natural form of consciousness, I should consequently awake with my heart thumping, probably remembering what I would describe as a beastly nightmare – one which need not resemble the actual facts at all – it might be that I *had* been run over, and the fright caused by such an imaginary happening could result in unruly beating of my heart, as fear generally reacts thus on the physical body. As we came to earth I saw the familiar setting I had so often seen in days gone by. It was a sunny evening and there were many people out walking. Children with their mothers or nurses were playing about as usual, and not far off I could see the constant stream of traffic, cars, taxis and buses that passed down Park Lane towards Piccadilly and Hyde Park Corner.

I suggested walking down Oxford Street, and although the pavements were crowded with late shoppers on their way home, and shop assistants just released from their day's work, we were in no way hindered. As before, I felt the strange gossamer contact, perceptible every time I was forced to pass through a physical body, and it was quite difficult not to apologize. My friend who did not like crowds, floated about two yards above the heads of passers by; I soon did the same and we came to earth again in Piccadilly Circus. 'Perhaps you would like to look at the scene of our last trip to London and see if you recognize any of the people in the foyer of the Trocadero?' he said. I agreed, and we strolled in. The lounge was just filling up with people waiting for friends, with waiters flitting hither and thither, taking and executing orders. I saw no one there whom I knew and no sign of either Charles or Roy Chapman; I wondered if the latter had become bored with the perpetual round of meals and drinks that did not have to be paid for, but I did not ask. My friend beckoned to me and I understood that he wished to go upstairs. I followed without question and soon we were in a corridor which had several doors leading off it. He entered one of these rooms, which turned out to be a bedroom, untenanted. We had of course gone through the door, so needed no key.

'Now,' he said, 'we had better be on our way. I came to this room so that we could be quiet, for I want you to realize that passing from the lowest sphere to the one less dense than this is quite a simple matter, only requiring an effort of will for it to become immediately effective. I want you to hold my hand and just wish to do what I do. You will not feel anything, but will notice that the scene around you changes gradually. The walls that seem to enclose us in this room will appear to melt, the furniture with which you are surrounded will slowly become vague and misty, and all the time you must let go, so that my will may dominate yours. Whatever happens do not be nervous for, if you panic at all you will very soon wake up in Colombo. Now are you ready?' I replied that I was, and I experienced no fear at all, only interest. I held the hand of my friend firmly and tried my utmost to allow myself to be controlled by his will, and almost immediately the walls of the room became blurred and indistinct; the same applied to the furniture and, in less time than it takes me to record, we were standing in the open air, in a small field, and in the distance there was what looked like a typical English village. 'Now listen,' he said, 'and you will hear very distinctly a distant rumble. That is the roar of London town and it can just be heard because you are only one sub-plane or sphere away from what is the actual astral counterpart of the physical London you know so well. This is the second sphere of the astral world and you can see already that it is very much less material than the densest part of that world – the part to which you go immediately after death. Let us travel a little and you will see what I mean.'

We started off, again floating gently a yard or so above the ground, till we came to the village which I had seen in the distance. It was very much like an ordinary village, for there were shops, two cinemas, a magnificent hotel which looked much too large for the size of the village and on the outskirts there were at least three buildings which were obviously churches. All around the village, stretching far and wide into the distance, I saw the most beautiful houses. Some were small, others larger, but every one was surrounded by a colourful garden in which flowers of every sort bloomed in profusion. I saw both women and men working in those gardens, but obviously working because it was a pleasure and not because they had to. Dogs of different kinds frisked about the lawns and the voices of children could be heard as we passed by. One difference between these and similar houses in the world was the absence of garages; and I noticed that there were no cars on the streets. It was explained to me that there is no need for transport, for people can get from place to place by much easier methods, as they only have to express in thought the desire to go anywhere, and immediately they float gently from where they are to the destination to which they wish to go.

I asked why there were shops when money was not needed. I was told that the people who find their happiness at this level like to live a life as near as possible to that they had always imagined as ideal when alive. 'Some spend money,' my guide said, 'they create it by their own imagination and they buy food which they prepare and even eat – all in imagination – because that is what they wish.' 'But surely,' I asked, 'it is quite unnecessary to have shops when a thought would be sufficient to produce in one's home what one wanted?' 'These shops,' he replied, 'have their origin in the minds of the inhabitants and none of them exists in the world, nor do the people who serve in them. Once the residents here think a thing, it becomes a fact in this world of illusion. These shops are all figments of the imagination, together with the things that are sold therein, but so long as the people want to have shops near to them, they have them, for they imagine them.' He continued: 'It is the same with churches. People like to continue their religious practices, even though after death they may have found that many of the statements made by their priests and pastors had not been entirely correct. The permanent inhabitants build these churches and ex-priests and ex-ministers of religion carry on their old vocations, drawing round them followers, just as they did in the life that has ended. Cinemas too are very popular, but whilst there is unending variety on the first sphere, it is not quite the same on the second sphere. Here, cinemas are not the astral counterparts of such places in the world, but are the creations, in thought, of the permanent inhabitants. There are always ex-producers of films, or amateur producers, who create new films in their imagination, and their thought-forms are produced on the screen for all to see. These shows are, in many ways, better than those we see in the world and those which astral inhabitants see on the first sphere for, under astral conditions, producers can allow their imagination to run riot. There is no need to consider the cost of production here. Theatres are also popular at this level. Those who are interested in amateur theatricals as well as ex-actors and actresses produce one play after another for the benefit of their friends and acquaintances and they are able to do so quite easily, as there is no difficulty in obtaining the correct costumes, scenery or an orchestra as these things are just created in their imagination and cost nothing.

'Some people still wish to live in hotels. Probably they are the people who have always thought it would be wonderful to live in one of the big hotels that were far too expensive for them in the world; now they can live in such hotels. That is why this hotel looks so very large compared with the size of the village. Such an hotel could not exist in an ordinary village in the world, but here it does not need to make a profit. People live in the hotel and have all the service and attention they want merely by imagining it, so they are happy – for a time.' 'But surely all this becomes very boring after a time?' I asked.

'Yes, it does,' he said, 'then the people look for something more satisfying in life, as you will see, for when their particular desire is no more they are able to change to something else, and get what they want. Many people are perfectly happy with this arcadian existence, particularly those who have had rather a hard time during their earth life – such people often spend ninety per cent of their astral existence under these conditions where they have the friends, pets, beautiful houses and gardens which satisfy them, and only pass on to the mental world when they are more or less forced to do so by the urge of their egos, who wish to progress along the Path of Evolution.'

My guide now told me to hold his hand again and join with him in willing to pass from this second sphere to the third. I did as I was told; at once the scene that surrounded us started to dim and gradually gave place to a new one. Our surroundings were now quite different, for we were standing in an open space, surrounded by what appeared to be dozens of small woods or coppices. If you can imagine a gigantic park with trees everywhere, with glades and dells intermingled with the clumps of trees, it will help you to visualize the scenery. There is nothing quite like it in our world, but I should imagine that from above it would appear as if one were over a gigantic Sherwood Forest. In many cases the open spaces were several square acres in extent, varying from a glade measuring perhaps three acres to open spaces covering what I would estimate to be a fifty acre field. All these glades were very picturesque, as everywhere there were flowering shrubs, while daffodils and forget-me-nots bloomed in profusion in the green grass. There were no houses to be seen at first, but later I saw odd houses, very large ones too, resembling the huge Halls or Manor Houses that one finds in England and which in the old days were inhabited by the artistocrats or squires of the county in which they were found.

We glided along and I saw that in many of these open spaces groups were congregated. We approached one of these groups and found that there were perhaps a hundred people watching an artist painting a picture, on a canvas that measured about fifty by thirty feet. They were obviously enthralled by what they were watching, for no one took any notice of us as we joined the group. The artist was not using brushes, but he had in his hand a long stick resembling a fishing rod and as he pointed the stick at different parts of the canvas, a picture appeared, first in rough outline then later in detail. As he painted, the artist spoke from time to time, explaining what he was creating. He made quite clear the impression that he wished those watching to have and, on one occasion, he rubbed out part of the painting – I cannot use any other word for, as he pointed the stick, a portion of the picture was erased – and explained that his previous thought-form had not been sufficiently detailed to get the effect he wanted. Again he seemed to concentrate, the rod moved up, down and across; a new detail which blended in with the rest of the painting immediately took form, and the second attempt at once emphasized the point he had made a minute or so before. I could not understand much of what the painter was talking about for it was couched in technical terms only comprehensible to a brother artist. I was told that the artist was one of the great painters of the past. My guide stated that an artist would paint because the urge which made him do so when in the world, continues after death. He does not have to use brushes and paint at this level, because he is able to express himself in colour merely by projecting the thought. The fluidic astral matter answers to the thought-form and the picture appears, as if by magic, as the thought develops. Although the canvas was huge compared with the pictures we have in our galleries in the world, it was in no way cumbersome to create a picture of that size at the astral level, when merely by concentrating on a particular part of the canvas, the picture within the mind of the artist came to life. I cannot describe the glorious colours of which that picture was composed, for we have no words to describe the many in-between colours that were used. When I mention that I saw at least thirty different shades of a colour, which if I described any of them I would have to call 'red', you will realize how impossible it is to give anything but a very incomplete description of what I saw quite clearly. My guide explained that many of the great painters of the past who were still at the astral level, lived in this sphere and that they spent their lives creating, in the form of pictures, the ideas with which their minds were filled. At the same time, the artists taught any who cared to watch and listen to them, the methods adopted in making pictures. I was told that it took only a few hours to create one of those huge pictures and it often happened that the artist, having finished one, started at once to create another. 'But does the first one fade, once the artist has withdrawn his attention from the canvas?' I asked. 'No,' replied my friend, 'it remains just as you see it now, so long as anyone is looking at it. You see, once a picture is created in astral matter, that picture remains static for anyone to see, so long as a single thought is concentrated on it. When all thought is withdrawn from it, then it gradually disintegrates into the main astral atmosphere and is lost for ever, or until a new thought creates it again as a new picture.'

I watched until the picture was finished, fascinated by the skill of the creator and the results achieved. When the artist had moved away and was talking to some of the crowd who had been sitting round watching him, I saw that several of the other watchers, obviously students of art, started to create something similar for themselves, taking the master picture (if I may call it that) as their pattern. I still watched and saw immediately the tremendous difference between their efforts and those of the great painter. It was explained to me that the reason for such a great difference was the lack of knowledge of the student compared with the knowledge of the master. The students were unable to express in clear thought what they wanted to appear on the canvas, so the results were decidedly amateurish. Obviously the canvas would only exhibit what they were able to express in thought, and I saw very clearly why that was so. Even in the picture galleries of this world, if one looks at a picture it often happens that one is able to feel something of what the artist has endeavoured to express. Such feeling is emphasized a thousand times at the astral level, and looking at the great painting I *knew* without any shadow of doubt what this artist wished to express in colour and form.

We moved off and saw many groups surrounding individuals doing similar work, but as the country was slightly undulating, it was practically impossible to see any two of them at one time. In one of the valleys where a slowly-moving stream trickled along, there was a group seated on its bank, seemingly doing nothing. As we approached, however, I realized that this group was not watching a creative artist, but was producing sounds resembling a beautiful symphony played by one of our world-famous orchestras. I did not hear anything until we got quite close to the group; then I found that the surrounding air was filled with the most beautiful music I had ever heard. In the centre of the group was a man whose face seemed familiar to me, yet I knew that I had never met him in real life. I asked my guide who he was and he whispered: 'That is the celebrated Johann Strauss.' At that moment he was demonstrating how the sound of trickling water can be expressed in music. I remembered that it was Strauss who had composed the 'Blue Danube' and this music seemed to have much of the lilt found in that hackneyed but beautiful waltz. It was even more beautiful still, I should say.

Whilst I stood enthralled, I saw on the opposite bank of the stream what appeared to be etherial figures, who in some way were part of the symphonic poem that I heard. My friend told me to look at these new people for: 'These are members of that parallel evolution I have told you about, the deva kingdom,' he said. 'But what are they doing?' I asked. 'And why do they look different from the crowds that are on our side of the stream?' It was explained that they looked different because the were indeed different. They are more etherial, because, being part of a different evolution, their bodies are different and, although made of astral matter, are at the same time less concrete than our astral bodies. I was told that these were some of the music devas, those beings who live and express themselves through sound, and that they were helping the composer, who was seated on our side of the stream, to express himself as he wished to do. Just how they helped I cannot say for they never spoke, but seemed to concentrate on the creator of the music and, through their thoughts, enable him to express in more and more detail what he endeavoured to create in sound. Volume of sound was there and every note clearly heard, but I found that when we passed from the group to a distance of perhaps fifty yards, nothing was to be heard at all.

It is difficult to describe these members of the deva kingdom in words that are understandable. Their forms were beautiful, but as they moved they seemed to vapourize, when they became still again they were once more quite definite in shape. I think I can describe it best by saying that the bodies seemed to be made of mist, which only held together in a concrete way when the individuals remained more or less still. We went over to the opposite bank, but as we approached these people they seemed to glide away, rather like shy animals. They had no fear of us, but did not invite contact at all and I felt that if we approached them with the intent to communicate with them (how that would be done I had no idea then) they would have vanished into thin air. My Indian friend said that this impression was in a way fairly accurate.

On my guide beckoning me to follow him, we moved on. Soon I saw that he was making for one of the large buildings, which I had taken to be a huge Manor House. As we drew nearer I saw that the architecture was very beautiful indeed and deep French windows overlooked the surrounding countryside. Spacious lawns gradually sloped away from the house, which was situated on the top of a rise. Flowers and flowering shrubs bloomed on all sides and in the distance, perhaps ten miles away, the sea could be seen if one looked carefully. It was a delightful spot; I wondered who lived here and for what purpose. We came down to earth on the terrace and entered the wide doors that led into a spacious hall, furnished as I would have expected it to be, but with one remarkable difference – that in the hall there were actually small trees and plants, principally roses I noticed, blooming indoors with the roots growing through the floor. There was no artificiality in this – in fact one felt one was in an indoor garden and the result to the eye was very pleasing indeed.

No one seemed to be about and there were no sounds of occupation, but my guide immediately led me to one of the doors that opened from the hall, and as the door opened sounds of music met my ear. There was only one occupant of the room, and he was playing a grand piano in a way which showed that he was no mean exponent of the art. He took no notice of us but continued to play and we listened, fascinated by the power of the musician over his instrument. There were a few very inviting easy chairs in which we sat down, and perhaps for a quarter of an hour the playing continued. As time passed, I seemed to recognize a similarity in this music to the Chopin Preludes, and in a whisper to my friend I asked who the musician was. 'Do you not recognize him?' he replied. 'That is the famous Chopin, who is still expressing his great soul through the medium of sound, in exactly the same way as he used to do when he was alive. You will notice, though, that he does not look delicate here, for when he was in the world, he suffered much and for a great part of his lifetime he was not a fit man. Now all that is changed: here fatigue cannot trouble him and he produces more and more beautiful music which, at times, he allows other musicians to hear. At this level there are concerts all the time, thus there is never any difficulty in attending these functions, if you are really interested and able to appreciate the beauty in nature that the musician is endeavouring to express in sound.' I looked at the performer more closely and found that I was unable to recognize any resemblance to likenesses of the great musician which I had seen, but my memory of these was vague and probably I had not studied them very carefully. He stopped playing after a time and turned round to us, in no way perturbed or annoyed by our presence. He assumed that we were music lovers, so explained to us what he had been trying to express and although he used some technical terms, I was fascinated by what he said. He emphasized that in his opinion every sound was a description of either colour or movement. Progressions and blending of chords were sound pictures of beautiful gardens, and where cadenzas appeared one should immediately 'feel' the presence of a slowly moving stream, perhaps between two perfectly laid-out gardens, and try to see the picture that the musician was endeavouring to express. I who considered myself musical, at once realized how little I knew of the true art, and resolved that after death I would be one of those people who took up the study of music in a big way. It is unfortunate that, in the world, these masters of music are in most cases entirely outside the scope and opportunity of the average man who has to earn a living.

We left as we had come, without any official leave-taking and, as we withdrew, Chopin turned towards his piano and recommenced to play. As we closed the door and were again in the passage, no sound whatever came through the door. There was only the sound of birds, many of which in divers colours flitted about, not only in the garden, but indoors also. My friend told me that this huge house was one of the great art schools which exist at this level of the astral world, and that hundreds of the permanent inhabitants of this world spend most of their time in learning something of the art in which they are particularly interested. I was told that tuition was always available, for all the great masters are willing to teach those who are anxious to learn, and that the opportunity is there at all times for there is no night or day and fatigue does not enter into one's calculations.

'But surely,' I asked, 'people do not carry on studying and practising day and night, week after week, month after month and year after year in this way?' 'Yes, they do, and as I have told you, they do not get tired nor does time hang heavily when they are interested and enthralled in what they are doing. If you analyse your reactions at the physical level, you will find that time never drags when you are doing *what you want to do*. Usually fatigue enters in and you have to stop, even though you are enjoying what you are doing, but here that does not apply as no one gets tired and there *is* no time as we understand that term; you do not have to get home for dinner, you have no wife waiting for you and you have no duties or responsibilities in any way. Those limitations just do not exist at the astral level, so the man or the woman carries on with the work or relaxation that he or she desires, without any thought of how much time can be devoted to that particular form of study or enjoyment.' My guide then told me that he had a little work to do, and politely asked my permission to leave me for a short while. 'Go where you will,' he said, 'no one will interfere with you and I suggest you wander in and out of different rooms, for I can assure you, you will not meet with any hostile reception. This building is very like similar ones which exist here and it will be well worth while for you to see more of what is done in such places. I shall return when I have finished my private work and I do not think you will be bored whilst I am away.'

From the outside I had seen that the building had at least three storeys so I decided that I would explore a little, as he suggested. To start with I went into some of the lower rooms. In one I found a sculptor with a class of pupils, explaining how a particular curve could be obtained. I stood awhile listening to his discourse and some of his pupils, without speaking, smiled at me as I listened, obviously not objecting in the least to my presence. In another room, a quartet was practising; in another a single violinist was going over and over a particular passage, with a score of music in front of him. It was very similar to an academy such as I had seen in the world, but with the great difference that there was no fuss or hurry and that all forms of art were represented, also it was very noticeable that the people concerned, although quite seriously studying, were so obviously happy and not tense in any way, like the students I saw the last time in the Royal Academy of Music in England.

Later I wandered upstairs and here I had a very pleasant surprise. As I opened a door (and I noted with interest that here one *did* open a door and did not go through it as one would with physical doors) and went into one of these rooms, I saw a girl seated on a settee near to an open grand piano. She had a piece of music in her hand, which she was studying. As I entered she looked up and at once I knew her, for she was Daphne Hillier whom I had last seen in England in 1935 when I met her at a golf club. The man who was my opponent that day knew her intimately; he introduced us and we soon got into conversation. I saw her many times during my leave and we got to know each other extremely well. I had thought several times of asking her to marry me for I imagined I was in love with her, but somehow I did not. For one reason, I did not feel that I had yet enough money to marry on, also I wanted to get to the top of my profession before I accepted the responsibility of a wife. I returned to Ceylon and for two years we corresponded regularly, then it all ended by her contracting pneumonia and to my great regret, her mother wrote to me to say that she had died. I wrote a letter of sympathy and gradually lost touch with the family. And now, there was Daphne before me, seemingly very much alive and looking just the same as when I had seen her last but with an even happier expression – in fact her whole face radiated joy and contentment, and some of the joy, I flattered myself, was at seeing me.

'Daphne, my dear, is it really you?'

'Yes, it is I,' she said, 'but what are *you* doing here? You haven't left the old world yet, I know, so what has brought you here?'

I tried to explain to her something of what had happened and why I was here. She said she was surprised to see me because, although most people who are evolved at all wander on the astral plane during the time that their bodies are asleep and recuperating for the following day, yet it is not common for living people to visit the third sphere of the astral world. In most cases they do not know how to get there, and very few know of the existence of these different levels. 'But darling,' she said, 'now you are here, you will be able to come again and we must see lots of each other in the future; there is much that I can show you. Although you never asked me to marry you when I was alive, I knew that you loved me, and I love you too.'

I then realized that it had not seemed strange at all for her to address me as 'darling' for I had so often called her that in the old days and she me, and although all that was several years ago, it came back in a flash and I felt again the same draw towards her, the same thrill at being in her company as I had felt in those old days. 'This is wonderful,' I said, 'and it certainly will not be my fault if I do not see a great deal of you in the future. Perhaps you will be able to help me in this, for I do not know whether I could get here on my own, even though it all seemed so easy this time when I had a guide to help.' I told her about my efforts in the recent past and how, apart from my first astral journey, I had not yet been able to bring anything through, even though I had tried very hard to do so. 'In future I shall want to remember what we say and do. I wonder if I shall be able to do that.'

As I said these words my Indian friend came into the room. 'So you have found each other,' he said, 'I thought you would if I left you long enough. It is just as well that you have found Daphne, for she can be of great assistance to you and through your love for each other, many things may now be possible that were difficult before. For one thing you will have a definite contact at this level, which you can concentrate upon as soon as you get out of your body at the moment of falling asleep. Your thinking of Daphne will immediately make itself known to her, for thought is a very powerful thing, and concentrated thought is not bound by different levels of matter, so

Daphne – if she will allow me to call her by that name – will know quite definitely when you concentrate your thoughts on her, in just the same way as people know that you want them when you ring them up on the telephone. Daphne cannot easily come to meet you, when you get out of your physical body and are on the lowest or first sphere of this world, but she can be your contact for passing from that first sphere to the third sphere, where you are now, in exactly the same way that holding my hand acted as a contact for you when I told you to will that you passed first from the lowest to the second and later on from the second to the third sphere. You will find that by the exercise of your will, plus having a contact who knows the ropes, there will be no difficulty at all.'

He continued: 'You see, you do not know very much about the law of karma yet, the law that to a great extent makes your contacts and gives you the opportunities which are so important to your evolution. This law of karma or law of cause and effect as it is usually called in Christian countries, deals with every word, thought and action of yours at the physical level. The mere fact of your having given affection at that level to Daphne and of her having returned that affection, even though it did not come to the natural fruition of what the world calls marriage, means that you two have a link with each other, which sooner or later you must work out. There is a great deal to be said for the state of being in love, for whilst a person is in that state or even imagines himself to be in that state, he wants to *give* and for a short period does not seek to get anything in return for what he gives. Expressed differently he exudes something that can be said to be the highest he can offer. That giving is a cause which must produce an effect; in other words, the law of karma must work its natural way. A real exchange of love makes an ideal partnership for progress in anything, for each one is only too willing and anxious to help the other in any way possible, so I welcome this contact of yours and I do not mind admitting that I hoped you would make it. I could not bring you here deliberately, for that would have been interfering with the natural working out of the law of karma I mentioned. Presumably it was your fate to meet again under these different conditions, and it is now up to you both to take advantage of the force of circumstances that has made this linking up possible. How fascinating is the working of God, of Fate. Had Charles not been killed, you would not have been so miserable that I was detailed to come and help you. Now, through your efforts to understand something of the evolutionary plan, you have been allowed to meet again a person whom you thought you had lost for ever – or lost for the remainder of your physical life.

'I cannot guarantee that on a morning following a joint astral plane expedition you will always recall all your experiences, for the development of a perfect memory covering what you do when you are out of your physical body, requires much practise and so far you are only a very young pupil. I shall help you to remember what you have seen tonight and when you write out your report of the night's happenings, you will realize how important it is to bring back into the physical brain cells the result of your wanderings; you will probably make a great effort in the future, which will gradually enable you to have the continuity of consciousness that is so essential. The mere fact that you have found someone in the astral world whom you were fond of in the physical world, will encourage you to make herculean efforts to overcome your limitations. Daphne can help you a great deal, too, for having lived at this level for some years, she knows the power of thought; she knows too what *can* be done at the astral level and what *can not* be done there. If you continue your efforts to remember what you do whilst out of your physical body at night, you will be able to carry on a second existence as it were, a life which you lead only when your physical body is asleep.'

Daphne then took up the conversation by turning to my friend: 'But Acharya,' she said, 'as you say I can be of great use to Henry now, why was I not able to link up with him before? I tried so hard after I came to this plane, but even in the early days, when I was living on the first sphere of this world, I did not seem to be able to make any impression on him.' Before he could answer, I interrupted and said: 'Look here you two, do you know each other? You called my friend Acharya and he has never even told me his name, though

I have seen so much of him the last few days. Is your name Acharya?'

'Yes and no,' my Indian friend replied. 'It is certainly part of my name, and I am usually called that, by those who have contact with me at this level. It is good enough for our purpose, so you too may call me by that name if you wish, but you soon realize that the names by which people are known in the world, at any rate the surnames, are not so important after all. You, Daphne, could not get in touch with Henry – do you, Henry, realize that this is the first time that I have mentioned your name? – because he was not yet awake in the occult or spiritual sense consequently he did not remember anything of what he had done out of his body, apart from stray dreams that were extremely muddled and incomplete; therefore when next he left his body, he had no concentrated plan, in thought, of what he wished to do. You talked to him, I know, but as you say, he did not seem as interested as when you talked to him in the physical world; when you expected him to remember what you had talked about a few nights previously, he seemed vague and dull. That was because he was not awake; it required some great tragedy, such as the death of his well loved brother Charles, to make him clamour for light, for occult knowledge; there had to be a crisis for through this, the urge to know is born – what a man really wants he can get, providing he is willing and eager to work. "Knock and it shall be opened to you", "Seek and ye shall find", said the great Master, the Christ, and those words are literally true. But now we must get on, for I have more to show you before it is time for you to return to your body. Perhaps you, Daphne, would care to come with us?'

'I would indeed,' said Daphne, 'for I know that with your knowledge and help I can go to places which I cannot yet visit with my limited knowledge.'

'First have a look at your watch,' Acharya said to me, 'and see how much time has elapsed since you left your body.' I looked, and found that the face of my watch was strangely blurred. I tried to imagine what the time would be and each time I thought, the hands of my watch changed to synchronize with my thought. 'I'm afraid I don't know,' I replied, 'for my watch seems to change the hour with each thought that passes through my head.' 'That is quite true,' went on Acharya, 'for you see, you are looking, not at an astral watch, but at the watch that you have imagined on your wrist. You are used to wearing a watch, so you automatically raise your wrist every time you want to know the hour; the mere fact that you expect to find a watch on your wrist, makes a watch appear on your wrist, for this is the world of illusion and what you think at the moment *is* for the moment. Now wait here and I will go and ascertain the exact time so far as we are concerned, for we are only interested in the time that exists in the place where your body is lying and to know when you are likely to have to return to that body. The time that rules in other parts of the world is of no interest to you in this case.' As he finished speaking, he seemed to vanish into thin air. I had hardly recovered from my surprise, when he was back again, standing beside me. He continued. 'I returned to your body, sleeping in your bedroom in Colombo, and the watch on your wrist there says 11.30.' 'But surely my watch must have stopped,' I said, 'for we seem to have been on the astral plane for hours and not just for an hour and a half.' Acharya continued, 'You will soon realize that time seems different at the astral level from what you are used to at the physical level. It is quite true that only one-and-a-half hours have elapsed since you emerged from your physical body and we started our tour, and you will appreciate even more what I say when, tomorrow, you write down your experiences and realize what you accomplished in just one-and-a-half hours of physical plane time. You must have had experience in your physical life when you awakened at 6 o'clock in the morning and realized that you had not to get up for at least another hour. You turned over, went to sleep again and had a long complicated dream that, in time, seemed to take a whole day. Then you awoke and your clock told you that you had only been asleep for twenty minutes. What I have told you is an astral fact, which you must remember, for time does not exist at this level.'

We then left Daphne's workroom and were again in the passage.

We floated down the stairs into the main hall and into the garden. No one seemed to be about, though we passed one man who was going into the Academy to carry on with his studies, for he had a case under his arm that looked as if it contained a flute. He smiled as he passed, but did not speak.

Acharya said that he wanted to take us to hear a special symphony concert which the deva kingdom was giving in a deep forest, in a remote part of the astral world where humans seldom penetrate. He told us that he had obtained permission for me and for him to attend and that he had no doubt that there would be no objection to Daphne coming along also, particularly as she was devoting a great part of her astral existence to the study of music. He explained that this concert would be quite different from any we had heard before, because its object was not just to produce beautiful music, but its specific purpose was building up a vortex of power that could be utilized for influencing a particularly important conference which was taking place in the physical world at the moment. He did not say what the conference was, but intimated that it had to do with the war and that the decisions which were made at this conference would have a great bearing on the eventual result of the war, also the date when once again the world would have stopped fighting and would have decided to try and settle its differences by negotiation instead of through the medium of arms and munitions. He explained that such force could be built up in two ways, through deep concentration and through sound. This blending of chords, brought about by means of each individual taking part in the proceedings concentrating deeply on the purpose to be achieved, built up a vortex of power which, when transmitted to the venue of the meeting through the medium of thought, actually influenced the people taking part in the conference. He gave as an example a group of people who were all irritable, some angry and all more or less worked up. Before opening such a meeting the chairman arranged for everyone to be served with a drink and to be allowed to smoke; at the same time he made sure that each had a comfortable chair, with the room warmed if it were cold to a temperature at which people felt relaxed. The meeting opened, the chairman perhaps started the proceedings by telling a good story, a second round of drinks was served and then the serious details of the agenda were tackled. What was the result? The people there, who a short time previously were feeling irritable and ready to disagree with each other, developed a camaraderie that made sensible discussion possible and the work of the chairman easy. In just the same way, but to a much greater degree, the force generated by such an effort as the deva kingdom was to make that night could be used to affect a group of men whose great influence could sway the destinies of countless millions of human beings. What they decided would indeed influence future humanity, so the work was certainly worth-while.

Without further preamble we then set off into the distance, floating about five yards above the ground and travelling at a speed of about fifty miles an hour. This part of the astral world did not seem to be occupied by human beings; I cannot remember passing any individuals or groups of people, as we sped upon our way. I noticed that the country was exceedingly beautiful and that from time to time we passed buildings, either near or in the distance, that appeared to be similar to the Academy which we had left a short time previously. There was a profusion of flowers everywhere and numerous trees studded the countryside. Here and there I saw dense wooded patches of country, but we were travelling too quickly to notice anything significant about them. I think Acharya did most of the talking and as far as I remembered he described the country through which we were passing, but my mind was so full with the wonders of my journey and what was still in store for me, that I cannot remember anything particular to record.

After travelling for what seemed like ten to fifteen minutes, I saw ahead of us what appeared to be a dense forest and I remember Acharya pointing out this landmark when we approached it, as the end of our journey. We did not however come to earth at the beginning of the forest, but floated some few feet above the tops of the trees for perhaps three or four miles, then – our progress having slowed down to something approaching a walking pace – Acharya led us through an opening in the trees, where I observed there was a most beautiful open glade in the form of a rough circle the diameter of which was possibly fifty yards.

As we came to earth, there was no sign of activity, nor could I see anyone or anything moving in the open space before us. We were led to a huge tree, the roots of which gave us most comfortable seats, and were told to sit down and remain quiet. It is perhaps opportune that I mention my impression of the light in this open space or glade. We were surrounded by dense trees, like an Indian jungle, whose tops seemed to branch out, so that the space at the top was very much smaller than the circle on the edge of which we sat. As I have mentioned, on the astral plane, the light is bluish grey, much clearer than the most perfect moonlight, but it has not the bright, direct effect that sunlight gives. Visualize this glade as being perfectly light in its entirety; if a rabbit had run across the open circle no one could have missed seeing it, until it had run into the thickness of the jungle. We therefore had perfect vision of everything that took place, and at the same time were surrounded by dense forest into which little or no light penetrated.

After sitting there for some minutes, I noticed a group of little men – like dwarfs – emerge from the forest on my extreme left, where they seated themselves cross-legged in a semi-circle. As far as I can remember there were about ten of them and each one carried with him an instrument which looked like a cross between a kettledrum and a tom-tom. I noticed they were dressed in little brown suits, with tiny shoes and caps made of a vivid green material, far brighter than the foliage of the trees. Their features appeared to be those of middle-aged men, varying from forty to seventy years of age, judging by earth standards. Those of you who have seen Walt Disney's film of 'Snow White and the Seven Dwarfs' will have quite a good idea of the appearance of these little men. They did not speak or make any sound.

Soon afterwards a group of much taller people emerged from the forest both male and female – an entirely different race. They appeared to be nearer to the human type, but were definitely ethe-real in appearance. The female members of this group were girls whose ages might have been from eighteen to twenty five, all had long hair either hanging free or tied with a blue or green ribbon. Both men and women were absolutely silent. This group numbered perhaps thirty-five in all and they carried with them instruments, obviously of a musical character, but slightly different from the violins, cellos, clarinets and flutes which we see in a western world orchestra. They did not sit down, but ranged themselves so that those with the same type of instrument were more or less together, whilst all formed a compact group, standing perhaps about twenty yards away from the first group of little men.

There did not seem to be a breath of wind, yet the top branches of the huge trees moved very slightly. An amazing silence prevailed for perhaps two minutes, then all at once the little men started to use their drums. Almost simultaneously they began to chant in very low voices, which blended with the background of the drums, without taking away from the beauty of the notes which came from the mouths of the little men. Obviously it was a spiritual chant or mantra, for the very air was permeated with the outpouring of force, which quite definitely they were endeavouring to create. After perhaps six verses of this chant, the second group, or main orchestra, commenced to play. It is quite impossible to describe the beauty of the music played, which blended perfectly with the back-ground of chanting and gentle drumming. The volume was not great, but it held one enthralled by its purity and beauty. What was being played was a symphony, for it had separate and distinct move-ments, with a main theme which was repeated from time to time. Two complete movements had been played and the orchestra was in the middle of the third movement when, suddenly, what seemed to be a human voice of astounding beauty rang out on the air. It seemed to come from above and immediately I looked upwards. At first I could see nothing and no one; after some time Acharya directed my attention to a distant tree on the opposite side of the glade and there at the very top I saw what appeared to be a young girl of great beauty, sitting on the branches with her hair floating behind her, taking the solo part in this most beautiful symphony of sound. She was a pure soprano, her voice had no great volume but the purity of each note sung tore at my heart strings so that I wanted to weep.

This went on for perhaps ten minutes, the orchestra playing a few bars, then the girl coming in with an unaccompanied solo, later passing to the ordinary method of singing in company with the orchestra, gradually building up the power for which the music was being played. A fourth movement which seemed to embody the spirit of the three which had preceded it, and entirely orchestral, closed the performance. The symphony simply faded away and suddenly one realized that the silence which had been so noticeable, surrounded us once again. I looked at the top of the tree where the singer had been – she was no longer there; the groups comprising the orchestra and the little men remained where they were, the members of the orchestra now seated on the ground. Out of the forest an old, old man appeared, he had a flowing beard and was dressed in ceremonial robes. He walked slowly and sedately to the centre of the open glade and raising his hands in supplication to some form of deity, started what seemed to be an invocation, for the two groups of players bowed their heads and listened to the words he uttered. I did not understand a word of what he said, yet I knew that it was a prayer, asking that the work which had just been completed should be successful. It was also an effort of will, for every member of both groups was concentrating to his or her utmost that the purpose might be fulfilled. It all ended quite suddenly and, silently, the old man vanished into the jungle, then the groups of players rose from their sitting position and moving down the glade disappeared from our vision. I was so affected by what I had heard that I did not want to move and it came as rather a shock to me when Acharya said: 'Well, that is all for tonight. I shall be most interested to know how much detail you remember in the morning.'

I was still rather in a daze when we stood up and, floating through the opening in the trees, began our homeward journey. Acharya gave us some idea of the purport of the ceremony we had just witnessed, but I am not very clear as to what he said for my mind was still in a whirl and I was thinking about the wonderful spiritual influence which had seemed to be the outstanding part of the concert from beginning to end. I remember though that he described the different performers; he said that the little men were nature-spirits, whereas the orchestra was composed of members of the deva kingdom, which is a parallel evolution to our human kingdom; the latter were similar in development in their scheme of evolution to Daphne and myself in the human kingdom. The soloist was in a different category for she was a very advanced deva and equal in that evolution to an exceedingly advanced individual in our evolution. The old man could be described as a priest, for he was dedicated to the priestly functions of that evolution and evolved through them, in a way very similar to that which happens in the human kingdom.

In due time we came to the Academy and stopped on the lawn just in front of the entrance because Acharya said it was necessary for me to retain a clear picture of this building in my mind for future occasions. I asked Daphne how I could find her again, presuming that I was able to get as far as this building by my own efforts. Acharya replied for her that I could usually be sure of finding Daphne in the same room that she had occupied when I first met her for, as there is no overcrowding in the astral world, most people can retain a particular working place for themselves. He however suggested to Daphne that she should show me the little cottage where she lived. Daphne was delighted at the suggestion, and asked us to come and see it. She led the way by floating over the top of the Academy, when to my surprise I saw what looked like a miniature 'Garden City' nestling in a valley about half a mile in the rear of the huge building. The houses, though small, were spread out, so that each little cottage had at least an acre of ground. It was quite apparent that each occupant had designed not only his cottage but his garden in accordance with his own particular type of tempera-ment and taste, and the result was exceedingly beautiful. There were cottages which might have been transplanted from any of the beautiful rural districts of England; others reminiscent of small villas in the South of France; others purely Italian in type whilst I noticed at least two built to resemble Eastern temples. Acharya noticed that I was interested in the different architectural types, so pointed out two cottages with domes similar to many Mohammedan temples I had seen, he said they were owned by people who were particularly interested in having a room with perfect acoustic properties.

Although I could have gone on gazing at this most wonderful sight, I sensed that Daphne was anxious to show us her home so, with her leading the way, we walked along a rustic path for perhaps two hundred yards. She led us through a gate into a garden, which was a veritable blaze of colour. The cottage itself could only be described as a dream house; the design appealed to me immediately. In front of the porch there was a little lawn, in the middle of which grew a shade tree with several wicker chairs arranged under its spreading branches – they looked so comfortable and attractive with their bright cretonne cushions. Immediately I was struck by the advantage in the astral world, in that as there was no danger of rain or robbers such things can be left outside for an indefinite period.

We went into the cottage and Daphne showed us first of all the largest of the four rooms that the cottage contained; it was furnished as a lounge with upholstered settees and easy chairs, occasional tables, other small chairs and a baby grand piano in the corner. There was no sign of ostentation but it was obvious that personal ideas of the owner had been given full rein, which in the world is often impossible, owing to the cost of things that we would dearly like to have. Here there was no such limitation and it was obvious from looking at this room that the owner was a person of artistic tastes, but with no desire for show in any form. There were several large windows, stretching almost the full length of the lounge, and the clear astral light which came through them brought out the beautiful blending of the colours in the tapestry that covered the chairs and settees and the colours of the Persian carpet that blended so harmoniously with the tapestry, upholstery and curtains. I realized that perfection was very easy to obtain at this level, if one had the right ideas. In the world one might search for years and then not find a Persian carpet that blended so perfectly with the other colours used in the decoration of the room. The walls which were an ivory colour, were bare but for a couple of etchings and one or two delightful water colours. It was a room in which one wanted to sit; it looked like a home and not a room for show. From just walking through the rooms, you realized the type of occupant who lived there and I could well understand Daphne wanting to show us her home.

The second largest room was furnished as a bedroom, a very typical woman's bedroom, with a divan in one corner and all the other details of furniture which one usually finds in a perfectly furnished room of this type. I was surprised that a bedroom should be necessary in the astral world, where sleep is not part of the ordinary routine of life. Daphne explained that, however, by asking me whether there were not occasions when I felt a desire to relax in a reclining position, merely to think or to read. I had to admit this was so, and Daphne told me that she spent very many happy hours relaxing on her divan, thinking, reading and making plans for the future.

The remaining two rooms turned out to be a library and a kitchen. The library was furnished with the same comfort and artistic taste as the other two rooms, bookcases filled with books all bound in beautiful Russian leather, completely covered two sides of the room. The mere look of the volumes invited one to sit down and peruse their contents. The kitchen was furnished with all modern appliances and although I had imagined a kitchen would be unnecessary here, Daphne said she still enjoyed making snacks for parties. Acharya again remarked that habits die very slowly in human beings and usually many years of existence in the astral world passed before these habits were entirely eradicated and forgotten.

I should have liked to remain here for a much longer time, but I could see Acharya was beginning to feel that the time was ripe for us to be on our way. I made one last request and that was to spend a few minutes in the garden. It was very delightful wandering among the flower beds, testing the scent of particular flowers and finding in each case that it was exactly the same as those flowers in the world, but perhaps a little more pronounced. Acharya commented on this point by saying that I should only be able to recognize a particular scent if I knew what to expect, for example if there were a flower which I had never seen before and whose scent was unfamiliar to me, I would only smell what I imagined the scent to be, judging entirely from its appearance whereas the real scent might be quite different from my imagination.

Daphne saw us to the gate, where we wished her *au-revoir*. I assured her that I would most certainly return to visit her, if I were able to find my way. We floated into the air again over the top of the Academy building, coming to earth once more at the foot of the rise on which the building stood. Acharya again told me to impress the outline of the building on my imagination so that I could make a perfect thought-form of it at any time that I was trying to reach it. This I did. Acharya then told me that it was time to return to my physical body in Colombo and that the machinery necessary to effect this transfer was the same as we had used when reaching this sphere of the astral world. He told me not to worry about it, but, simply to make an effort of will and endeavour to make a thought-form of the lawn outside my bungalow in Colombo. He held my hand as he had done previously, but he told me that this was merely to give me confidence and was quite unnecessary. I started to concentrate with all my might, and as I did so, I noticed that my surroundings immediately became blurred, and although there was no actual wind resistance noticeable, I had the feeling that I was moving through space. Instinctively I closed my eyes, holding the thought-form of my garden in mind, and after perhaps a few seconds, the feeling of movement seemed to cease. On opening my eyes, I saw Acharya standing beside me on my own lawn outside my bungalow in Colombo, smiling at my obvious surprise. We immediately entered the bungalow through the locked front door, went up the stairs and through the door of my bedroom, it no longer amazed me that neither of these doors offered any resistance. Sure enough my body, which I had left so many hours previously, was still lying asleep on the bed, but it seemed to show some slight signs of restlessness, which Acharya explained was the normal reaction of a body when the time approached for awakening. He said I would awake in a very short time and emphasized the necessity for me to sit down and record immediately the details of the happenings of the night that had passed. He placed his hand just above the top of the head on my body and appeared to concentrate upon the brain cells – so that they should give me the necessary assistance in remembering. I do not remember saying good-bye to Acharya, nor have I any recollection of his leaving the room, for within a few seconds I felt the urge to return to my body very strongly within me and, with the slithering movement which I had noticed on a previous occasion, I slipped into it again and at once was wide awake.

Thank heaven, the memory of the night's happenings was still with me, so I immediately got out of bed, put on a dressing gown and moved over to my desk to commence the record of my journey. It was a quarter to six, and I found it necessary to switch on the electric light, as it was not light enough here for me either to write or use my typewriter. The report has taken a considerable time to complete, but as I had carefully arranged beforehand that I was not to be interrupted, I was able to finish it in peace and without any outside distractions.

Having breakfasted, I read through my report to make sure I had not forgotten anything. Tonight I mean to make an attempt on my own to get back to the third sphere using the Academy where Daphne works for my landmark.

I am really excited this time, for I have something to report. Not that I accomplished anything very wonderful, but at least I had some success. After returning from a walk, I felt physically tired and gradually prepared for bed. I read for a few minutes after getting into bed, then turned out the light and settled myself for sleep. I still remember so clearly what my body looks like lying on the bed that it was no longer necessary for me to visualize myself in a hypothetical mirror, as I had been taught to do in the early days. I don't remember slipping out of my body, but sure enough, there I was in my room, with my body lying on the bed, as I had seen it on previous occasions. I went out of my room through the door, down the stairs and out of the front door on to the lawn where Acharya and I had stood not so many hours previously. It could only have been about half past ten, for there were still people about, walking and driving along the road; I realized that what I was seeing was the astral counterpart of the cars and of those people, and that I was actually on the lowest or first sphere of the astral world.

Now to make my attempt to get away from that first sphere up to the third sphere where Daphne is living. Now to concentrate the whole of my effort of will and make a thought-form of the Academy, which Acharya made me visualize so carefully early this morning. I closed my eyes and used every ounce of willpower that I possess and, sure enough, the feeling of movement without any wind resistance was the same. I kept the thought-form of the Academy very clearly in my mind, willing myself to reach the spot; and all at once I seemed to feel the sensation of movement had ceased and I opened my eyes. Thank heaven, I'd done it! There stood the Academy on the top of the hill, just as I had seen it last night. My excitement was almost too great to bear. In fact I must have lost control of my faculties entirely; for suddenly everything around me including the Academy became blurred, and the next thing that I remember was waking up in bed in my physical body in Colombo, with my heart beating thirteen to the dozen.

Oh God, I've messed it up entirely! I got there! I actually reached the place where I wanted to be and through my excitement and lack of control I'm back again where I started, wide awake. I must have lain awake for at least two hours, cursing my stupidity and lack of control, then I seemed to settle down again and become sleepy. I decided to have another try and this time to keep control of my faculties so that I would not return to my physical body before it had had its normal quota of sleep.

Once again I concentrated on getting out of my body, at the same time I kept before me the thought-form of the Academy building. This time my exit from my body was a little different from the first occasion. I have no recollection whatsoever of standing in my bedroom, as I did earlier in the night, but to my amazement and great joy I found myself on the same spot from which I was so ruthlessly dragged when I lost control, a few hours before. This time I remembered that control was necessary and somehow forced myself to remain calm. I know that I sat down on the grass making no effort at all to go near the Academy, but just concentrated deeply on steadying my heart beats and remaining cool and collected.

Then I rose to my feet and floated up to the main entrance of the building, up the stairs and to the door of the room which I remembered so clearly had been occupied by Daphne the previous night. This time I realized that there was no possibility of going through the door in the same way that one does on the physical plane, for this building was composed of astral matter and therefore a door here was an obstacle to one's progress, as I also was in astral matter. I knocked on the door and waited, but there was no response. Once again I knocked, wondering whether the noise I made was insufficient for the occupant to hear, but again complete silence reigned and the door did not open. After a little time I carefully turned the handle and shyly peeped in. I need not have worried for there was no one there. I recognized the room though as the one where I had met Daphne the previous night, so without further preamble, I closed the door again, floated down the stairs and out of the front door. Rising in the air I passed over the roof-top and proceeded on my way, in the hope that Daphne would be at her cottage. I came to earth before I reached the garden city and had another look at its beautiful setting. It was indeed rather like a glimpse of Paradise. No wonder that I had wanted to remain looking at it for a longer period last night. There were even more types of bungalows that I had realized, and I absolutely thrilled at the picture set out before me and only wished that I had been an artist, so that perhaps, after returning to my body, I could have reproduced some semblance of what I now saw in such detail.

The garden city occupied an undulating valley and on all sides the ground gradually sloped upwards until it reached a row of hills, plainly visible in the distance. I gazed my fill at the beautiful gardens which could only exist in a world where there were no limitations of labour or wealth. There was much to be said for the cultivation of imagination in our physical plane existence, for although day-dreaming did not produce any practical results whilst we were alive, yet the faculty of being able to imagine in detail most certainly came into its own in the astral world. Here one only had to be able to visu-alize a thing and think strongly about it for the thought to become at once an established fact, a fact which remained just as long as, though thought, one wished the idea to continue. Happy people indeed and the thought passed through my mind that, now I knew a little more of what might be in store for me, I would not fret if I were told that soon it would be my turn to leave the physical world; what I had seen and knew, made me realize that it is always possible for people who have left the world to be happy, if they really desire happiness. My last thought before an unforseen interruption occurred was, how easy it was to form a picture in one's mind of almost every occupant of the bungalows. In the physical world it would be wrong to judge a man from his garden, for probably he has had little or nothing to do with its creation. Here no gardeners are necessary, each garden was the creation of the owner and from it one could make a very good guess as to the outstanding character-istics of the individual. I wished I might have the opportunity of putting my theory to the test.

Just then my attention was drawn to a figure in white, running towards me along the rustic path, a figure that was shouting as she ran. It was Daphne of course and she was obviously very excited. 'You've got here, Henry, I'm so glad. I've been trying to help you so much during the past few hours and I thought my efforts had been useless. Some time ago I felt once that you were near me and I was almost sure that you had managed to get through the veil, but the impression gradually faded and I had given up hope, when once more I felt that you were in the vicinity. I *had* to come to this spot, I don't know why, and when I saw you standing here, in a reverie but really here, I think my heart stopped beating for a moment for sheer joy.'

I looked at the graceful figure before me. She seemed just a slip of a girl, dressed in a muslin frock that showed off her girlish figure in the most enchanting lines, and I marvelled at her beauty. Her dark brown hair with golden tints running through it made a perfect frame for the animated expression on her beautiful face, the eyes of which showed a love so pure that few men see it in the world. Everything that was decent in me seemed to come to the surface and I felt the age-old desire to protect, to hold and to keep, which is the true feeling of a man for his chosen mate. I had no desire to speak, but gently though firmly took her in my arms and reverently pressed my kisses on her face and hair. There was no passion in my embrace. There seemed no room for passion, but there was a deep seated desire to come into closer touch with this child of my dreams, a desire to know her better and if possible to add to the happiness that she already had. She returned my kisses, not at all surprised at what I had done. For a moment her eyes filled with tears – tears which at once I tried to kiss away, almost before they had appeared. Then she hid her face as we turned and with my arm around her waist, slowly strolled in the direction of her cottage.

When we got there I led her into the lounge and up to the piano. 'Play to me darling,' I said, 'I feel the need for music just at the moment.' I pulled up a chair and seated myself beside her. She played – what I cannot remember, but I know it was something that depicted joy. I leaned back, closed my eyes in sheer ecstasy and for a few moments realized the peace that passeth understanding which, once felt, makes any other sensation empty and imperfect.

I don't know how long we talked, but I remember I told her all about my misery after Charles was killed and how Acharya came to me, also my experiences up to the evening before, when with his help I met her again. We decided that although we were divided by the two of us living at different levels of consciousness, which made an ordinary life together impossible, we would create a life together, with things as they were, and prove that death was in no sense a barrier either to progress or happiness. We both felt sure that our regard for each other must enable me to pierce the veil whenever necessary and that I would come to her, even though she could not come to me.

She told me something of the people who lived in the valley. Many of them were friends of hers, whom she wanted me to meet. She explained that people at this level linked up together, where their interests were similar, but that there was no marriage in the ordinary sense of the word. People there were known by names, but they were christian names or nicknames, never surnames. She gave me instances of some of them, mentioning that one girl who was always smiling and happy was known as Sunbeam. Another who always dressed in blue was called Bluebell, whilst a man who made his life there one long effort at helping other people was known as the Doctor. I said I would look forward to meeting these friends of hers, but how would they take to me, to one who could not belong in the ordinary sense of the word? 'You will see,' she said, 'at this level you only see the nice side of people, for there are few petty jealousies such as we have in the world; everyone can have whatever the other person has, if he or she wants it, merely by making a thought-form to that effect, so any striving to live up to the standards of others is unnecessary. People here become themselves and you will soon realize, when you know them as they really are, that the old saying "there is so much good in the worst of us and so much bad in the best of us" is proved to be very true.'

I hadn't the slightest idea how long all this conversation had taken, but I remember I began to feel a stirring within me which told me quite plainly that my body had had its quota of sleep; I had just time to bid Daphne good-bye when without further warning the walls of the room in which we were sitting seemed to melt into a mist which instantly evaporated, and again I felt that sensation of moving through space. At once I was awake in my body in Colombo; there was no half-way break on this occasion – I didn't find myself in my bedroom with my body lying on the bed in front of me; I was wide awake and looking at my watch. I saw that it was 7 o'clock and the sun was shining into my room. At once I got out of bed, almost rushed to my desk to start my report of the night's happenings, and now I have finished. It is 10 a.m. and I have just time to shave, bathe and have some breakfast before I may expect Acharya. I wonder what his reaction will be to all I have to show him. Will he be pleased at the progress his pupil has made, or will he tell me that this is just a flash in the pan – that it is unlikely I shall be able to travel alone in the future, and that much more hard work and study are necessary before I can wander without guidance. I shall know very soon. The picture of Daphne is still very real. Perhaps I missed my happiness by not marrying her in England when I had the chance. I don't know, but I have no regrets. I feel that perhaps there is a future before us which is infinitely more fascinating and beautiful than anything that could have been our lot in the world.

CHAPTER EIGHT

It must have been about 11 o'clock, and for the last ten minutes I had been sitting at my desk reading over the notes I had made of last night's happenings, when suddenly the pleasant voice that I now know so well broke into my reverie.

'Well, Henry, my friend, so you have accomplished something worthwhile at last. Now perhaps you will admit that you have been able to prove for yourself those things which I told you in my early talks were facts to me.' It was Acharya who had entered my room in his usual unobtrusive manner.

'Yes, Acharya, I am bound to admit that. I am beginning to realize that even the things you have told me about in past talks and which I have not yet been able to prove conclusively, are undoubtedly provable with more experience. I suppose you are well aware of what happened last night and it is not necessary for me to hand you my report, but I would like you to read it, so that you may check up and see if I have forgotten anything of importance.'

Acharya replied that he was only too willing to read my report and that he wished also to see the record of the second astral journey which we took together. He added he would talk about them for a little while, before passing on to more tuition. After finishing these records, his face showed his appreciation of my efforts – he was obviously extremely pleased that I had been able to put into actual practice some of the tuition he had so patiently given me during the past week or two. I told him how much I was in his debt for his unselfish and much-needed help, but he assured me that I need not feel in any way indebted to him, for cases like mine were his particular job in life and that he was well rewarded if those he taught benefited from that teaching in a real and practical way.

He then started to comment on the past two nights and I listened most attentively. This is what he said: 'I must first explain why I took you to the third sphere of the astral world via London; as you know this was quite unnecessary. My reason for it was to make you realise that any town in the world which you might go to in your astral body, looks the same as the physical town you are familiar with, though what you *see* is not physical, but the astral counterpart of the physical places as they exist on the *first sphere* of the astral world. In future it will be better to start your journeying from Colombo. You will find it just as easy to get up to spheres higher than the third, which is where you made contact with Daphne, as the same machinery operates, but to do this it is necessary to have a particular place on each sphere, which you visualize in thought and to which your astral body will be transported in the course of a few seconds of time as you know it here.

'I expected that you might possibly become a little afraid when your surroundings became blurred and you felt a sense of movement; I must congratulate you on not having experienced an initial failure, which I have noticed sometimes happens to my pupils. They become frightened, and almost simultaneously awaken in their physical bodies, with beating hearts produced by their fear. Actually you have experienced this, for last night you returned to your physical body for a time without having any intention of doing so, when your excitement got the better of you whilst making your attempt to reach Daphne without any assistance from me.

'It is unnecessary for me to say anything much concerning the *second sphere* of the astral world, for it is very like the first, only less crowded and less noisy. In the two spheres nearest to the physical world, the permanent inhabitants live more or less the type of life that has always appealed to them in the physical world. In most cases such people do not remain there for the whole of their astral existence. There are exceptions who are so attached to the material existence, that they have no desire to progress to the higher spheres of the astral world – but they are forced to do so after a period that might run into two or even three hundred years, at which time the ego urges the vehicle he is occupying to pass through the "second death" to the mental world. This method of progress is not the usual one and it would not be yours when the time comes for you to pass into the astral world. You have already realized from seeing the activities of but a few people who live on the third sphere, that the life there would appeal to you considerably more than a round of visits to restaurants, theatres, or cinemas.

'I was able to show you both artists and musicians at work in the *third sphere*, but you must realize that this sphere is not limited to artists or musicians and it would have been quite as easy for me to show you great engineers, craftsmen devoted to some particular trade, in fact every type of individual whose consuming interest in life is not bound up with purely material amusements or pursuits.

'When you were listening to the music played by the group under Johann Strauss, you saw a few members of that parallel evolution called the deva kingdom. When you have had experience of spheres higher than the third, you will find that not only are they much more numerous there but that they cooperate more and more with members of the human evolution the further we get away from the material life. You may think that their existence is preferable to ours; that you would prefer to evolve from fish, butterflies and birds into the stage of elemental, nature spirits and eventually to a stage of deva such as you saw comprised the orchestra that performed in the wood. We cannot change our evolution, except in very exceptional circumstances.

'You probably wondered why I spent so much time at the Academy, showing you the work that goes on in buildings of this kind. I did so for two reasons: the first reason was that you should realize that this was but one of the many schools which exist in the astral world, where people can get tuition in the particular art in which they are interested – tuition which enables them to be born in their next life with a desire to continue to study along these lines, so that a few of them at least can become great masters of their art and help the physical world to progress in both culture and learning. My second reason you must have guessed for yourself. Through your having such a clear picture of that Academy in your mind after you had returned to your physical body in Colombo, you were able to get back to that spot quite easily and without any stupendous effort; from there you were able to contact Daphne and continue your astral plane experiences. Do not forget this for the future. Pin-point a certain building or view in your mind and you can then use that pin-pointed picture as a thought-form on which to concentrate, when you desire to go to that particular sphere of consciousness.

'I hope that you have realized very pertinently the necessity of knowing the way in which time affects your sojourn at the astral level. I went into detail over this important point, so that you should understand how to investigate, should the occasion arise.

'Our journey to the part of the astral world where the ceremony was being held requires no comment. You will remember that after we arrived there and seated ourselves on the roots of one of the trees at the edge of the open space, I warned you to be as quiet as possible. The reason was that although the members of the deva kingdom do not really object to any human seeing them at their work, they do not like interruptions of any sort. You will have noticed the intensity of purpose that prevailed throughout the whole ceremony. The little men or gnomes, who came out of the forest in the early stages and started the proceedings with their chanting and beating of drums, are on a much lower level of evolution than both you and the members of the orchestra. One thing though must have been apparent, that all of them seemed to be concentrating with their whole strength on the work in hand. There was no levity or chatter such as one is used to at a concert in the world, immediately prior to the performance. It is this remarkable difference that I wish to impress upon you, for if you are to understand the members of the deva evolution and, I trust, in due time work in conjunction with them, you must realize that life is a very serious business to them and levity does not usually enter into their proceedings. Not that they are unable to laugh; they are indeed extremely happy people who seem to enjoy the simple pleasures of nature but they do not allow outside influences in any way to disturb the perfection of the work to which they set their hands.

'In order that you may understand what follows, I must digress for a few moments. You have probably heard of initiates, arhats and adepts in our evolution. These terms occur in occult books, but little has been written about them. Briefly I can tell you this much for the moment. As man evolves along the road that is set before him, he is actually under the control and guidance of a group of adepts, who are perfected man, but who were as you are, countless thousands of years ago. These men have finished the course of lives to be lived at the physical level, for they have learnt all the lessons that the physical world has to teach. Because of their developed love for humanity as a whole, they have elected to remain (at some sacrifice to themselves, as you may understand later on) in connection with this planet, to help it on and to assist in its development. These adepts are sometimes referred to as masters, because some of them take pupils, men living in the world and not yet perfect in any sense of the word, to help them with the work that has to be done. These pupils are given many opportunities of development which are not open to mankind in general, but you may be sure that they have earned these opportunities and it is not in any way a question of favouritism that they have been picked out from the bulk of humanity for this special work. It is hard work and usually means that such men have to give up many of the things they would do in the world, in order to devote themselves exclusively to learning how they can help humanity, without receiving any material benefit in return for that work. It is selfless service that they offer, and their only reward is that they are allowed to contact personally, in sleep when using their astral bodies, these perfected men whom they have agreed to serve.

'Such pupils, after many lives of work and special training, are prepared for Initiation ceremonies. These ceremonies give them powers that make them different from the ordinary run of human beings. They teach a man how to read other men's minds, for by the time that such a man has developed to this state, he will never use that power for anything other than to help a fellow human being. He is taught how to have continuity of consciousness at all levels – as I am teaching you to have continuity of consciousness at the astral and physical levels only; that is something which is difficult for you to understand as yet. Such men can, if necessary, work what the world calls miracles, but this is never done, except on the instructions of one of the adepts who help to govern the planet. There are five stages of initiation and only when the fifth is reached is a man perfect and free from the necessity of being born again into the physical world. Sometimes the lives of initiates are extended, so that a man lives long beyond the normal span, but this is only done for special purposes or because that man is needed in a particular country in the world, to wield an influence which may make a difference to future generations.

'During the deva ceremony at which you were present, you noticed that the young girl who took the solo part in the symphony remained at the top of one of the tall trees on the edge of the glade and did not at any time approach the members of the orchestra or come down to the ground. There is a reason for this. These girls are trained especially for the work they do; they live apart from the main body of the deva people and are in fact dedicated to their particular work. For this they have to develop extremely sensitive bodies, and minds that can attune themselves to the particular object which is being carried out. This girl, for instance, is a highly evolved being, she is an initiate in her evolution and so has knowledge and powers, far greater than the average type of deva whom you will meet from time to time.'

'Then there was the priest who completed the ceremony and invoked the Beings who control the universe, to help the work that was being done. He too was a highly evolved being, but nothing near an initiate and probably not even a pupil of one of the perfected men. His calling was that of a priest, who has been taught to gather up the force that has been generated by the concentrated music and the concentrated thoughts of those present and to transmit it through the power of thought to the meeting being held in the physical world. You may perhaps not believe that such things are possible and there is no necessity for you to do so, but to say "Such things cannot be" is just as foolish as believing only became someone else has assured you that such and such a thing is true.

'I welcomed the opportunity Daphne gave us of seeing her little cottage for I knew that at certain times she would not be occupying her room at the Academy. Also I was glad for you to see that there were many people living in the valley where Daphne's cottage is, for I want you to meet and talk to some of those people. Your story and the efforts you are making to live a life apart from your body whilst still living in the world, will not only be interesting to some of them, but it will help them also. Some are not as evolved as you are and have not had, in past lives, the opportunities for progress which you had, and which have led to your being given special tuition in this life. Because you have been privileged to be taught, you too must be willing and anxious to pass on any knowledge that you have, to others. Your intention of publishing the gist of my talks with you and your wanderings out of your body as a book is a good thing, but that will only help others who are still living in the world. What I tell you now, and in future talks, is not for your ears alone, but for the ears of anyone who is interested enough to want to understand. When you are told things that have to be kept secret, it is usually because the possession of such knowledge would enable men to do harm to others, if such knowledge were used for selfish purposes, but I can assure you that you are never left in doubt about such matters at the stage in development when that type of knowledge may be given to you.

'This brings me to the end of your record covering the second astral journey, and I must congratulate you on the details you were able to bring through. Your determination to remember was the reason for your success and if you will only realize that will-power is, to a great extent, the open-sesame to most of your difficulties, you will continue to have success in the future.

'The only important detail that you did not seem to remember, and which you probably did not realize at the time, was that during the ceremony in the open glade, there were several hundred members of the deva kingdom floating gently – more or less hovering – immediately above the open clearing and perhaps some fifteen to twenty feet above the tops of the trees surrounding the glade. They were not merely spectators or a congregation, such as we see in a big church in the world, but they were most certainly active participants in the ceremony through whose efforts, mainly, the necessary force, of which I have spoken, was generated. It would have been interesting if you had seen them, for you would have noticed that at the end of the invocation made by the bearded priest, they seemed to gather up the force for good that had been generated and immediately afterwards moved off in a compact body, presumably to ensure its achieving the desired results. Do not let this lapse on your part worry you in the least, for I can assure you that you have done very well indeed.

'The urge you felt to try things out for yourself, the following night, was quite a natural one, and whenever similar urges impress you in the future, always act upon them immediately. The urge comes from the ego, which is you, and the ego is only too willing for you to progress in knowledge of this kind. Activities on higher levels than the physical are much more interesting to an ego than the artificial amusements and the normal routine activities that we have to go through in the physical world. The ego of course realizes that our physical plane lives are necessary for his progress in evolution; but the goal of this ambition is always the same – for man to emancipate himself and to learn as quickly as possible the lessons that our countless lives are meant to teach us. By doing so he will all the sooner be free from the necessity of being reborn again, and be able to take up a different and much more interesting existence, such as is only possible for someone who has learnt all the lessons that have to be learnt through the medium of physical existence.

'You can see for yourself how much easier it is for me to explain things now, as you have a fairly good idea of the life that people live on the first, second and third spheres of the world next to this. The third sphere, as you have seen, provides most of the schools for training students in the different arts, and very soon I shall show you the fourth sphere which is really a continuation of the third. The first and second spheres form one stage, the third and fourth the second stage, the fifth and sixth the third stage, and the seventh sphere is the frontier between the astral and the mental worlds.

'On the *fourth sphere* we find many musicians and artists, who work alone and do not wish to teach or perhaps have finished teaching for the time being. We find doctors doing research work. A number of new remedies to fight sickness and disease are discovered at the astral level. Many groups of research students get together and exchange ideas; although they do not have any physical guinea-pigs to work upon, their theories are in due time perfected and impregnated upon the minds and brain cells of doctors doing similar work in the physical world. If you were to ask any medical man engaged in research in this world, whether he had at any time awak-ened in the morning with the germ of an idea – which possibly would take him months to perfect and put into practice, but which eventually became one of the new advances in medical science – he would probably admit that such was the case. There are buildings, both large and small, which seem to be what we would describe as mental hospitals. Although astral life makes it possible for any normal human being to be completely happy, there are still large numbers of people who cry for the moon and want the impossible. They worry, as they worried in life, and a form of mental neurosis is the usual result. The astral body not only includes a counterpart of the human brain, but it also includes within itself a mental vehicle, commonly referred to as the mind. A man can be troubled by his mind after death; remorse for hasty actions and words in his past life, which he now realizes can never be entirely obliterated, cause him a certain amount of suffering, intense or otherwise, according to the sensitivity of the individual. Such cases are often treated by doctors who specialize in mental troubles, with great benefit to both doctor and patient.

'On the *fifth* and *sixth spheres*, you will find still more research workers, such as psychoanalysts and brain, heart and other specialists.

'It is quite usual for doctors and specialists in different branches of science to live many consecutive lives in which they carry on with the same type of work; you can imagine how invaluable it is to such men to meet their confreres at the astral level, where all knowledge is pooled in the interests of humanity. There are groups of philosophers who wish to help the world in their particular way; they feel that if the trend of thought in the world were changed to more progressive lines than wars and national domination, life would be considerably more comfortable and more desirable. There are mystics who believe that mankind can best be helped by meditation along such lines as the "Unity of Life". There are other deeply religious beings who feel that man can advance only if he is attached to some religious belief or dogma; such men endeavour to produce a perfect religion by taking points of doctrine from all the great religions of the past and present and blending them into a new philosophy. The devas concern themselves deeply with all this work – as you will see for yourself in due time.

'On these levels world economic problems are discussed and worked upon for months and years. When certain conclusions are arrived at by these specialists, remedies are tried out by means of impressing these conclusions upon the minds of human beings living in the world who are in positions where their advice will by acted upon by nations or powerful groups of reformers, for mankind must be helped when crises in the world are too great and too serious for them to solve by their own endeavours. In periods of crisis great world leaders seem to stand on a pinnacle and shine – often a man who previously was but a humble politician or leader of a party arises and becomes a prominent figure in world politics; wisdom and leadership far above what would normally be expected of him is the result, which all can observe. When the crisis is over and his great work is finished, such a man seems to go back into his former obscurity. Such men *are* chosen and they are helped by one or other of the great Beings who brood over this universe for the benefit of mankind. Whilst the period of overshadowing lasts, they are indeed supermen; but when the crisis is over, this overshadowing has to be withdrawn for each man has free-will by right and may only be helped so far and no further.

'On these levels there are men who are interested in the growing shortage of food for a humanity that is increasing by millions each year. Devas help with their problems by suggesting new methods of cultivation; these suggestions are put into the minds of those living in the world who are responsible for such problems in their particular regions. In this way, new ideas and methods come to light and are gradually adopted by mankind. You will be able to attend some of the conferences which take place in these spheres and prove for yourself that what I am telling you is indeed true, but it is not likely that you will be able to remain at such conferences until conclusions are reached, for they often go on for weeks or months, calculated by your idea of time, and naturally you will have to return to your body after a few hours away from it. Great progress is often made at such conferences and suggestions are made to people living in the world, which enable humanity to advance in all its different ways.

'You probably have wondered why the world progresses much more quickly one century than another. It is not only that distances have been obliterated by air travel and such things as wireless, but simply because mankind in general is slowly but surely becoming more interested in solving existing problems, and by such solution the masses benefit. In other words, the more evolved men are becoming more and more unselfish, which proves that they, at least, have learnt some of the lessons that lives in the physical world are meant to teach us all.

'It is difficult to explain the work of the deva kingdom, for the methods used are so very different from those to which you are accustomed. To understand it at all, you have to remember that the deva kingdom controls to a large extent the part of life we call Nature; the seas, the winds, the use of the sun in cultivation and such things as the correct times of the year for planting different seeds, are all part of the particular domain of the devas. They join in discussions with members of our evolution, when their specific knowledge and experience can be utilized. Usually they transmit their thoughts through a mental process and not through words – but they can use the medium of speech when it is necessary for them to do so. From time to time you hear in the world of a tornado, a cyclone or an earthquake that leaves in its wake much loss of human life, devastation and thousands of homeless. You may have wondered why a beneficent Providence could allow such things to happen, but have you looked for the possible reason of such tragedies? Is it not true, that previous to such devastation, men and women have been living in those places under conditions which breed crime instead of progress? A tragedy such as I visualize, could easily be the means of awakening a slothful government to its responsibilities and often a rebuilding scheme is at once commenced, so that those who remain alive may be housed under conditions considerably more favourable than before. The devas control these cyclones and earthquakes and I know from personal experience that their pity for a humanity which, through its blind-ness, makes such disasters necessary, is great indeed. They allocate large numbers of their people to meet those unfortunates who lose their lives through these disasters, as they pass from the physical to the astral world, and do all in their power to minister to their fear and help them acclimatize themselves to their new conditions. It is the same when world wars take place and innumerable souls are slung out of their bodies by modern weapons. There are insufficient astral helpers belonging to our evolution to deal with the rate of killing that accompanies an army advancing against heavy opposi-tion, so members of the deva evolution take their places side by side with men, to do what they can to help the many who are terrified at the moment of their passing. It is indeed true that there are times when men and angels (devas) walk in unison, each serving God to the utmost of his being.

'I must now tell you a little about life as it is lived on the *seventh* and last sphere of the astral world. The first thing that will strike you, when you visit that part, is the complete absence of buildings of any sort. There are no signs of human habitations at all, but you will find that there are permanent residents living at this level, although they do everything in their power to discourage contact when other humans approach. Such men are of the opinion that their progress in evolution can only be accomplished by resorting to complete seclusion and a life of silence. In the physical world there are holy men, who live apart from humanity in out-of-the-way places at the foot of, or at the top of, lonely mountains where humans seldom penetrate. These men spend their whole lives in meditation, fasting and living what the world would describe as an ascetic life. Such men are the same after death and in due time they make their way to the seventh sphere of the astral world, and continue their lives of meditation there. You will find men who during their earthly lives as monks or friars were members of brotherhoods which enjoined absolute silence and a life apart from other normal human beings. These men have become so used to living within themselves, praying for long periods for the helping of mankind that after death they derive solace in continuation of the same existence that they lived for so many years on earth. There is no necessity at the astral level for any such persons to seek for a cave or build themselves houses to live in. Neither food nor accommodation is necessary to their existence, so they usually live in the open, in woods and out-of-the-way places, where they are most likely to be left alone and undisturbed.

'In addition to the humans who live at this level, you will find countless numbers of highly evolved members of the deva kingdom who carry on work but have no contact whatever with the members of our evolution.

'You will also find those human beings whose sojourn at the astral level is over and who have to pass through this seventh sphere in order to reach the mental world through which they must pass on their journey back to the higher part of themselves, the ego, who has his natural habitat on the higher spheres of the mental world – called the causal level. These humans are usually accompanied to the seventh sphere by guides, who are men like themselves but more evolved and older souls; the particular work of these guides is to explain, in detail, what is meant by "the second death". The journey from the astral world to the mental world is entirely painless and is merely the dropping of another sheath. The guides make it their business to eradicate any fear that might arise in the minds of these people, for although we have all travelled the same journey many times before, after each physical incarnation has been completed, yet we do not remember those previous journeys, because for each new physical incarnation we have entirely new mental, astral and physical bodies, which do not carry with them detailed memories of past lives. The passing from the astral to the mental world is some-thing outside the control of the average individual and, when his time comes, he is forced to drop his astral body for the simple reason that he has no further experience to gain at the astral level; he must then pass to the mental world in order to consolidate the mental work that he has accomplished during his physical existence and add it to the reservoir of knowledge, contained within the perma-nent atom, representing all his previous lives. Having received all the necessary information that can be given to him on the subject of his passing, the man gradually falls asleep and awakes almost immediately in the mental world, having during that brief moment of sleep dropped his astral body for ever. Friends meet him in the mental world in exactly the same way as friends met him when he passed from the physical to the astral world. He commences an entirely new type of life; in the case of the average man this is usually much shorter than his life in the astral world, though the duration is longer for evolved men.

'The astral body which has been left behind by the individual who has passed on, takes some little time to disintegrate and return to the main mass of astral matter. During the period of disintegration, the body retains a likeness to the individual who previously occupied it. You must understand that it is only a shell, yet owing to the fluidic nature of astral matter, it can move about and to an inexperienced person seems to retain a semblance of life. I have seen people who have visited this seventh sphere during their physical plane exist-ence, nonplussed at finding that they are unable to get into conversation with some of these shells which they find floating about. A shell is not a corpse in the sense that the physical body after death is a corpse because, although it has no connection whatsoever with the real man, the ego who has dropped it, yet it still contains a little life. Indeed until the disintegration is complete, the shell must think of itself as a man, for it is a fragment, a shadow of the man who is gone. At spiritualistic seances we sometimes see manifestations of various sorts when, instead of the sitters getting into touch with the man himself, they only contact the shell – this can happen when the man has been dead a long time – a friend of a sitter seems to come back and talks to them, yet in various ways he does not appear to be as intellectual as he used to be; he seems to have deteriorated. That is impossible; a man does not deteriorate, he progresses on the other side of death, so whenever one comes in contact with such a case, one may be sure that it is not the real man at all but only this frag-ment, this shell he has left behind. Although a shell is inanimate, it is quite possible for other creatures to enter it, to take it on as a tem-porary body and play the part of the original man. This is often done by astral human beings who enjoy playing practical jokes, and by playful nature-spirit who may take hold of one of these shells, put it on as one would an overcoat, and masquerade in it. The man masquerading inside the shell will very likely give "proof" of his identity, for whatever entered the brain of the original occupant during his lifetime will have passed into the astral counterpart, and it will remain there for the use of any entity masquerading in that body. In many cases a certainty may be acquired by an investigator who is sufficiently clairvoyant to see what is behind the shell, but whoever is investigating needs to take great care, for even the shell from which the fragment of the man has disappeared can be galvanised into activity within the aura of a medium. You may come into contact with shells some time in the future; one thing you can be quite sure about is that they are in no way dangerous and can do you no harm.

'This concludes my talk for today. You have undoubtedly realized that it completes my very brief survey of life on the different spheres of the world next to this. I want you to prepare a list of questions for me to answer tomorrow morning. After that, when you have had several days of experimenting on your own, I shall visit you again and tell you something about life as it is lived in the mental world. I shall not be able to give you as much detail of this world as I have been able to give you about the astral world, because it is much more difficult to provide analogies of what takes place in the mental world and compare them with similar things that take place in the physical world. Life there is so very different from here, for everything has to do with *thought*. Here you have tables and chairs and buildings. In the astral world thoughts are the tables, chairs and buildings – in fact there is nothing there but thought – so you can well understand my difficulty. I shall probably take you on a short visit to the mental plane also, in the hope that you will be able to remember something of what you *sensed* rather than *saw* there, but I shall tell you more about this in future.

'I shall come again tomorrow at the usual time when I hope your list of questions will be ready.'

CHAPTER NINE

I had a wonderful night's sleep; I awoke this morning at the usual hour much refreshed, but without recollection of anything having happened during the night. My list of questions is ready, and I hope Acharya will not consider it too lengthy.

I was re-reading my questions when the door opened and Acharya greeted me with: 'There is no need to apologize for the number of your questions; I have discouraged your asking questions regularly because I knew much would become clear to you with personal experiences at the astral level, and too many interruptions do not help either the speaker or the listener. I shall do my best to answer your question in language which should clarify your difficulties.'

Q. 'In your talks you have never mentioned anything about the conventional Heaven, to which the bulk of Christians are taught to aspire. Is there such a place or does it only exist in the imagination of the priests and ministers of religion who insist on its existence?'

A. 'There is certainly no such place as Heaven, but there is a state of consciousness, which is often referred to as heaven by the people living under those conditions. Some people argue that the state of consciousness is found in the higher stages of the astral world, whereas others insist that it is found in the mental world only. Some people argue that there is a difference between that which is called Paradise and that which is called Heaven. You will remember that the Christ, speaking to the penitent thief, is reported to have said: "This day shalt thou be with me in Paradise." Paradise was the name given by the Greeks to the upper regions of the astral plane and they taught that Heaven was found in the mental world, after man had left the astral world on his journey back to the home of the soul or ego. At these higher levels some men surround themselves with the thought-forms of Seraphim and Cherubim, in strict accordance with the ancient Hebrew scriptures. It is perfectly real to them and it harms no one if they are content to think it all real, so why worry them? Many of them even make thought-forms of God or St. Peter, and nothing that you could say would convince them that they are living in a state of illusion. There will come a day when they have developed their intellect a little more, when they will begin to try to ascertain what is fact and what is illusion.

'I notice that although you ask about the conventional heaven, you have not mentioned the conventional Hell. That of course no more exists than Heaven exists, but usually one does not find people in the astral world making thought-forms of a conventional Hell and living under such conditions, for no one is ever so self-critical as to be quite sure that Hell is the right place for him. Most of the people who live surrounded by the thought-forms of their idea of a conventional Heaven are only too happy to exist in such circumstances, as they feel they have either earned the right to be there, or have been extremely lucky to find themselves in a place for which they were not quite sure they had qualified. A conventional heaven created by people living at the mental level is quite different – thought it serves the same purpose for the people concerned.'

Q. 'You said in your third talk that you would explain the difference between an animal's life in the astral world and the life lived there by a human being. What is the difference?'

A. 'There is a considerable difference between the life of an animal in the astral world and that of a human being. In the case of the former, it seldom inhabits spheres of that world higher than the third, for the life that a man lives on the higher spheres has little interest for an animal, and only in exceptional cases does a human being take a favourite animal with him when he passes to the higher spheres. An animal certainly has a short sojourn at the astral level after each physical life has been lived, but it does not usually last for more than ten to fifteen years at the most. When the time comes for the group soul, of which the animal is a part, to reincarnate in new animal bodies, the animal entities which have been living separate existences at the astral level, are again drawn back into the group soul and their separate identities at once cease to be. The group soul, when its various parts return to it, is coloured by the experiences of those several parts, and the life-force of which the group soul is made up then splits itself into sections again, each section inhabiting a new animal entity, and further experiences are gained in these new bodies. As I have explained to you previously, this goes on until the group soul is ready to individualize as a human being.

'Those few years that an animal spends in the astral world are always happy – even in the very rare cases where a dog dies from a broken heart, because its master gave it away or left it with strangers when he was forced to go on a long journey; such an animal quickly finds a new home. In the astral world you never see a dog ask for food whereas you have seen for yourself many humans continue to eat and drink after death, merely because they have formed the habit of so doing. A dog or a cat only eats when it is hungry and seldom from greed. At the astral level it doesn't get hungry, so it never asks for food. A dog of the hunting species has during its life been trained to hunt; after death it continues to do so. Its instinct is to look for its quarry and that very looking is in itself a thought, so a quarry immediately appears and the dog at once chases it. Whether it catches it or not is of little importance, for the quarry which is only a thought-form cannot be killed in the ordinary sense of the word, but the dog enjoys the chase and its life continues to be a happy one.

'A horse which during its lifetime has been a favourite hack of a natural lover of horses soon finds another owner with a similar love of his kind and the same routine goes on with benefit and pleasure to both horse and rider. In some cases, after a favourite animal has died, its owner in the world thinks strongly about it, when he goes to sleep at night. The animal feels the "call", and sometimes is able to contact its late owner and share a few hours of his company. Unfortunately this is not a desirable thing, for the horse or dog feels the loss of its late master when such a person has to return to his physical body after the sleep period is completed, therefore it is kinder that they should be allowed to attach themselves to new masters or mistresses. There are rare cases where the affection between a human being and his pet is so strong that the group soul, of which the animal is a part, is in its way linked with that human being. This can only happen towards the end of the group soul period, when it is divided into only two parts, awaiting time for its individualization as a human being. Because the human being has done so much for that group soul, by helping to eradicate the last vestige of fear from animals attached to him, the entire group soul, consisting of two dogs or two cats for example, has two or three consecutive lives in the same household. In this way the time when individualization can take place is often considerably shortened. I could tell you of authentic instances of this happening, but my time is limited.

'The period that an animal spends in the astral world is too short for the conditions ruling there to influence deeply the evolution of the group soul, so when that period is over, the animals disappear from the homes to which they have attached themselves, to return to their group souls for new incarnations in the physical world, where further experience is gained.'

Q. 'Why is it that Charles did not contact us on the second astral journey? Is it that he is no longer interested in me, owing to his new life being so very different and more thrilling than the physical one, or can he not join up with us without your assistance?'

A. 'I am very pleased that you have raised these queries, for though it will take me some time to explain what you want to know, it is most necessary that you should be clear as to why opportunities of movement at the astral level vary for temporary visitors and permanent residents. Whilst physical life continues, the astral body is an auxiliary body, but it is used by you during sleeping hours for activities in the astral world. That body, composed of astral matter, has particles in it relative to all the different spheres of the astral world, and so long as you have a physical body, these particles are intermingled one with the other. You are able to travel to any sphere of the astral world up or down merely by exercising your will-power, and, in accordance with the sphere to which you go, these particles of your astral body become active and make such journeys possible. To make it perfectly clear, when you are sojourning on the first sphere, the particles relative to that sphere are at that time active, but when you pass from the first sphere, for example, to the fourth, it means that the fourth sphere particles become active, whilst the particles relating to the other spheres remain dormant, so long as your activities are at that fourth sphere level.

'As long as you have a physical body, this process goes on, but when the physical body is dropped at the moment of death, the astral body, which before was a mass of revolving particles all intermingling, rearranges itself into an entirely different form. In order that you should understand this perfectly, try and visualize the astral body after death as an ovoid, like an orange, with a core and with seven separate and distinct skins surrounding that core. The core represents the permanent atom relating to all the different spheres of both the astral and the mental worlds. The seven skins are composed of matter relative to the seven different spheres that exist at the astral level, of which you now know something, and, at the moment of death, the astral body so rearranges the matter of which it is composed, that the outside or densest skin is made up of atoms similar to those which you require to function on the first or densest sphere of that world. When, after a period of time, you leave the first sphere and pass to the second, you drop that outer skin, leaving the atoms relative to the second sphere of that world, which now become active, on the outside of your body. The same thing applies when you pass to higher levels. In passing, each outer skin drops away and leaves the skin beneath it, which at once becomes active and enables you to be fully conscious in the sphere to which you have passed. Now if you wish to pass down again from, let us say the fourth to the first sphere, it is necessary for a permanent resident to call upon the atoms contained within the core of the orange – the permanent atom – in order to effect that change. This requires a much greater effort of will than in the case of the temporary sojourner, for he must draw round his astral body yet again a new skin relative to the astral matter of this sphere in which he wishes to function.

'Charles did not accompany us on our second astral journey because I did not invite him to do so, therefore he did not know that such a journey was contemplated. You can now realize that, had we taken Charles with us on that journey, it would have been necessary for me to explain to him in detail the machinery that would have had to be employed to enable him to get back to the first sphere where he is still living. It is not because Charles is finding life at the astral level so full that you have not seen him during the past few days, but simply that the average individual who lives in the astral world does not hanker after contacts with people living in our world, in the same way that you wished to make contact with Charles immediately after his death. You ask if Charles could join up with us without any assistance – most certainly he could, providing he thought about us sufficiently strongly to make that desire known to us. He could for example wait in your bedroom every night if he wished, for the moment when you pass out of your physical body; then he could make known to you his wish to accompany you, wherever you go. He has not shown this strong inclination, so you have not had any contact with him lately. In case you are worried, let me assure you that Charles, at the moment, is busy with a temporary attraction which he has for a member of the opposite sex, who has recently died; he is very happy showing her around and proving to her how much more he knows about conditions than she does at present. My suggestion to you is to leave him alone for the time being, as I think that later you will link up with him again for your mutual benefit.'

Q. 'You have not mentioned why some people are born cripples and others blind. Others again deaf and dumb. Is there a reason?'

A. 'There certainly is a reason and my few remarks relating to the law of karma, or cause and effect, should have answered the question for you. It is essential for you to impress quite clearly on your mind that all such tragedies are produced entirely by the individuals concerned, by their actions in previous lives, and are not due to an evil Creator who likes to see humans suffer. A child is sometimes born a cripple, because in a previous life he was the cause of extreme suffering to another human being or to an animal. A man may, in a drunken rage, beat a child so cruelly that the beating produces a physical deformity, which medical science is unable to cure; this would undoubtedly cause such a man to be born a cripple in his next life and so be forced to suffer in something of the same way. People are sometimes born deaf and dumb for the reason that, in a previous life, they had been unfortunate enough to be a parent of a deaf and dumb child when, instead of making family conditions happy for such a person, the parent showed his disappointment at having a child which was abnormal by taking it out on the poor creature, who could not defend itself, thereby making life much worse for it than it need have been. Even evolved beings who know the reason for children being born cripples or abnormal in any way, sometimes fail to realize that having an abnormal child is an exceedingly fine opportunity for them to make good karma, by treating it with much sympathy and understanding. You may argue that justice today is very different from justice in the past, but the unthinking actions of our past lives must be paid for, even though in those past incarnations man was less sensitive to pain than he is today and used to much more ruthless treatment. Do not forget that it is the *intention* which decides the amount of suffering.

'Similar karmic consequences follow on emotional and mental cruelty. Quite often one sees a mother, who is a widow, putting obstacles in the way of a son marrying, merely because she selfishly wishes to keep the boy within the family circle. The parent argues that the marriage would cause inconvenience or less revenue to the family household, or that she is too delicate to be left alone, so the boy, through a sense of duty, gives up the chance of a happy marriage and selflessly devotes his life to looking after the selfish parent. He does not always realize that the parent is selfish – though it is a fact for anyone to see. The karmic result of such selfishness is that it must be considered as only fair, if in a future life this woman would fall in love with someone, only for that person to die, or be killed, before the marriage could take place. After many years, recovering from this loss, this same woman finds that another individual has fallen in love with her. There appear to be no reasons why things should not work out right on this occasion, but Fate may again take a hand in the game of life, with the result that one of the contracting parties develops an incurable disease, which puts marriage out of the question. As people do not know the reason behind such happenings, they are inclined to think that the person concerned is a plaything of an unkind Creator – but such is not the case, for you cannot suffer in any way unless you yourself have produced the cause for that suffering.'

Q. 'Why are some people born under "a lucky star" with plenty of money, good health and every seeming advantage, whereas others are born in the slums, with no natural advantages, and often with disease inherited from their parents?'

A. 'The environment into which every man is born is made by himself in a previous incarnation, also in accordance with the law of karma. When a man is born under what you call a "lucky star" with lots of money and perfect health, the world naturally feels that he has indeed been blessed by a Divine Providence – but this opportunity of an easy life is only accorded to one who deserves it. The man who is born in the slums, with many limitations and perhaps hereditary disease is considered unfortunate, but I can assure you that he too has earned what he receives. To find an instance of a man who has earned the right to be born with a "silver spoon in his mouth" you have only to look amongst the poor people of the world to find examples of this kind. How often have you seen generosity by an individual who is not blessed with many of this world's goods, but nevertheless goes out of his way to assist others less fortunate than himself? Such a person is only too often taken advantage of by unscrupulous people. Generous actions such as these people perform earn for them the right to be born in very different circumstances in a future existence and they very seldom lose the opportunities which great wealth provides, for they continue to help their fellow-men as they did in the past, with benefit to themselves and the world. If these opportunities are wasted, then the man makes bad karma instead of good, and it would have been better for him had he been born into circumstances less favourable from a worldly point of view.

'It is not necessarily a great misfortune for a man to be born in humble circumstances. In such cases he has the opportunity to overcome the limitations of his environment through his own efforts. We often see such men surmount the obstacles of their birth and emerge successful, even leaders of their generations. It takes courage to do this, yet the efforts made not only improve a man's character, but enable him to make much good karma in that incarnation. His efforts and his refusal to be deterred by those natural limitations will usually ensure that, in the life to follow, his environment will be much more favourable.'

Q. 'Can you explain why some races are born with coloured skins and others with white skins? Is a man with a white skin always more evolved than a man with a coloured skin? Is it a good thing for individuals of different races to marry? Is a white man ever reborn into a coloured race once he has inhabited a white body?'

A. 'From a spiritual point of view there is no reason to suppose that a white skin is necessarily better than a coloured skin. The colour of a man's skin does not denote his standing in evolution, it is usually due to the climate prevailing in the country in which he is born. The question of which nation a man will be born into is usually decided for him, though the ego is given a certain amount of choice. Before his return to physical life begins, the ego is shown the particular characteristics which he lacks and, because each nation has special characteristics of its own, expressed by practically all the members of that nation, an ego is usually born as a child of a family forming part of a nation whose predominant virtues and characteristics that ego lacks, in order that these may be built into his future structure.

'Many thousands of years ago the parts of this planet which were principally inhabited by men were the countries where you now find the indigenous people having coloured skins. Although Australia is today a white man's country, the aborigines of Australia were black men. In South Africa the original inhabitants were dark-skinned people and although there are large numbers of these still living, South Africa today is controlled by the white man. All of us have in our early incarnations occupied dark-skinned bodies. As civilisation advanced, the countries now known as the West became inhabited, and in order that these countries should be developed as quickly as possible, the perfected men who supervise the rise and fall of nations arranged for some of the more advanced egos in the world to be born as children of the pioneers who first inhabited Western countries. Because the climate in these countries was generally much colder than the climate in the Eastern countries, the sun had less effect on the skin of these individuals, with the result that white races came into being. Progress today emanates mostly from Western nations and, because of that, it is desirable that the most experienced men in the world, the older souls, should be born in Western bodies. Great Britain has been the ruling nation for the past century or more and has therefore received her due quota of advanced egos, but now America is taking over the responsibilities of that difficult position. It is certainly not chance which decides whether a man is born an Englishman, an American, a German or a Chinese.

'It must be obvious to you that *all* men with white skins are not more evolved than *all* men with coloured skins. Every nation in the world requires a certain number of experienced and evolved egos to lead it and help with its progress in evolution, so a certain number of old souls are always born into *every* nation. Take for example India; in that country you find millions of unevolved beings, but you also find a large number of intellectual, advanced beings and many extremely spiritually minded men. India has always been a country whose inhabitants thought a great deal about spiritual development. Believe me, it has an ancient culture and it will also play a great part in the progress of the world in centuries to come. Obviously it is necessary for such a country to have egos born into it who can guide the destiny of its countless millions so that in future years it can play the part allotted to it.

'Whether individuals of different races should marry is a difficult question to decide. It may sometimes happen that individuals who are born into different nations have been linked in past lives, through marriage for example. When these people meet in this life, as members of different nations, the attraction which drew them together in the past may still be as strong as before. In some cases it might be advantageous for such people to marry again; only by investigating the individual past experiences of both parties could one give an opinion that would be of value. I feel though that usually it is most undesirable for white men to marry coloured women, or the reverse, for the habits and culture of the different races do not mix well, therefore such a marriage does not work out to the advantage of either person. The result may also be that half-caste children are brought into the world and it is apparent that sometimes these suffer from the accident of their birth.

'A man who is born in a white body does not necessarily return to earth as a member of a white population in his next incarnation. This again is a matter of karma and of many circumstances so that no general reply can be given to a question of this sort. In the case of a white man who, through a feeling of superiority, exploited other members of the human race, merely because they had coloured skins, the law of cause and effect would come into action. He would probably be forced to be born into a coloured race in his next incarnation, so that he might learn the lessons of tolerance and understanding, which he so obviously lacked in his former existence.'

Q. 'You have not said what happens to a man who commits suicide. Is such an act a great crime?'

A. 'The taking of one's own life is not only a crime, but is also an extremely foolish act. You do not solve your difficulties by running away from them, but merely postpone their solution for a future life. A man would argue that the circumstances which he has to face are the cause of his getting out of life, whereas they are the circumstances which have been judged necessary for his progress in evolution and he must go through them sooner or later. In exactly the same way that a child who plays truant from school will be kept back in the lower form for another term and until he has realized that in order to qualify for a higher form he must obtain at least a minimum number of marks in all subjects, so when the man who commits suicide returns to the world in his next life, a group of circumstances will again arise, forming exactly the same obstacles and difficulties from which he now runs away. He must then face them and overcome them, for if he runs away once more, he is merely delaying his own evolution, and until he has faced and overcome these obstacles and thus learned the lessons they were meant to teach him, he cannot advance any further on the journey towards perfection. Extreme remorse usually follows an act of suicide, and within a very short time of their arrival in the astral world, the majority of suicides would give anything to undo their action. Unfortunately they cannot go back, but must wait until the time arrives for their next incarnation, and they are left in no doubt whatever that in their next life they will have to face the same difficulties again.

'Because the man suffers so much from remorse and because he would give anything to get back into his physical body, even though it would mean facing up to the consequences, he often refuses to make the effort of will necessary for him to get rid of his etheric vehicle, which you will remember winds itself round the astral body at the moment of death. On account of this clinging etheric vehicle, he is what is known as "earthbound" just so long as he remains obstinate and refuses to get rid of it. Being a suicide he does not get the same sympathetic help from the astral helpers as you have seen is selflessly given to all who pass to the next world in the normal way; thus he may *remain* "earthbound" through ignorance, being unable to function properly either in the physical or in the astral world, feeling the extreme loneliness that exists under these circumstances. After a period which seems like an eternity, he will, through a changed state of mind, draw towards him a helping hand, after which he can commence his life under astral conditions.

'The exceedingly unpleasant conditions ruling in that 'no-man's land' sometimes make a man so bitter against his Creator and mankind in general, that he wanders about the place where he took his life, trying to influence other people to do the same thing. The reason for this is the awful loneliness of his present condition, and he feels that if he can persuade others to do what he has done, he will not be entirely alone in his misery. On very rare occasions he succeeds in his efforts and the karmic result of such a deed means that he must suffer greatly in the life that is to come. Suicide is *never* a release, only a postponement, and no circumstances in the world are so bad that a man should resort to such methods of evading them.'

Q. 'If there is a god or deity controlling our lives, why does he allow wars, particularly as the majority of mankind desire peace?'

A. 'Why do you suggest that wars are made, or allowed to be, by a Creator? Wars are quite definitely the result of man's actions and his aggressive tendencies. There will be wars so long as there are separate nations in the world and while some nations wish to rule and exploit other nations. There is national karma as well as individual karma and the groups of people who have banded themselves together as a specific nation and have interfered with the life of another nation must always bear the consequences of such actions, whether good or bad. In many cases a nation will argue that it meant well for the peoples whom it conquered, but history has usually proved that a conquered nation never quite settles down under the heel of a conqueror, nor can it evolve as quickly as when it is left alone to work out its own salvation.

'Wars beget wars and so it will be, until mankind realizes that all members of the human race are members of the same human family, who should be treated with sympathy and understanding and be given help as a matter of course. In due time there will be no separate nations for all men will live in harmony together, each group exchanging with others the things which the part of the world in which they live can most easily produce, together with the manufactured articles which their training has enabled them to perfect. Separate nations will then become merely states in a world nation and wise men, drawn from each group, will govern and legislate for the good of all. It is quite true that the majority of men desire peace, but unfortunately peace or war is usually decided by those who happen to be in power at the moment. The responsibility of any nation or any group of men for launching a war such as we are passing through at the moment is great indeed and it is seldom, if ever, that such a war can be justified, whatever the arguments may be that are put forward in an endeavour to prove that there was no other way out. The world will soon realize that even the nations which win modern wars, lose in the end and after a war the conditions ruling in the world are so difficult, that any advantages they seem to gain are outweighed by the post-war problems they must face. Never think that wars are desired by the powers that control Creation. These perfected men do everything in their power to lead humanity along the paths of peace and progress, but their efforts are limited, because man has been granted free will. That is his peculiar heritage as a member of the human kingdom.'

Q. 'When people are very evolved, do they automatically achieve the continuity of consciousness which enables them to remember what they do whilst out of their bodies during sleep?'

A. 'My answer depends on what you conceive to be an evolved man. The average man has from five to six hundred incarnations in different bodies, during the time that elapses between his first to his last life as a human being, having then passed the fifth initiation and become an adept. Although about six hundred lives are usually necessary to learn all the lessons that this world has to teach, it is only during the last fifty lives or so that a man develops occultly and learns to use the faculties latent in all men, such as intuition, clairvoyance and the power consciously to get out of his body, whenever the necessity arises. For all general purposes you can assume that an evolved man has developed these faculties. But it possible for one not so evolved to be given the opportunity of developing along this particular line, and your own case should serve to illustrate my point. You probably have more than fifty incarnations in front of you, before you reach the stage of a perfect man, but because your need was great, you have been granted special tuition and in return I hope that you will show your gratitude by passing on this knowledge to others less fortunate than yourself? If you continue to work as you are working now, you will find that your memory of what happens to you when you are out of your body becomes clearer and clearer, and your knowledge of the life beyond the grave will enable you to progress much more quickly than is usual. At the same time it will bring you much peace and contentment of mind. Do not imagine that having been able to develop this faculty, you are different from, or superior to, many others who probably would have welcomed a similar opportunity to yours. Pride is always a danger, for it is often responsible for help being withdrawn from an individual, with the result that such a man falls back into the Slough of Despond.'

Q. 'Are we born an equal number of times as men and women or is sex just chance?'

A. 'Your last question is an easy one. No, sex is not just chance and we are not born an equal number of times as men and women. It is only possible to develop certain characteristics in female bodies and others in male bodies. By the time we reach perfection, we shall all have developed to a minimum extent all the virtues that add up to the ideal of a perfect man, and much more than a minimum in some of them. A man who develops through action naturally is a different character from one who develops through leading a saintly life and through a capacity to meditate for long periods in an endeavour to help his fellowmen. All types of perfected beings are necessary, and many are the ways taken by us to fulfil our destiny. If an individual should lack courage and the capacity to make sound decisions and to rule faithfully over his fellow men, it would probably mean that such a person might have to be born in a male body for two or three consecutive lives, so that he would have ample opportunity for the development he needed. If on the other hand an individual lacked the instinct called maternal (or even paternal) and also was incapable of that selfless devotion and capacity to love a person, even when that love was spurned, it would probably mean that a life or two in a female body would be desirable, so that these lessons might be learned, In theory one should inhabit the same number of male and female bodies in the total number of lives which we live, but in practice it does not work out that way, for some people develop more easily in one type of body than they do in the other. In due time, when a man reaches perfection, he should have all the outstanding qualities of both sexes reasonably well developed. When you have an opportunity of meeting some of these perfected men, you will find that what I have told you is indeed true.'

Acharya continued: 'This brings me to the end of your questions and after you have transcribed your shorthand notes and read them through, I hope you will find that the answers I have given clarify the points you have raised. If I were you I should have an early night for you must be tired, and I would not bother about concentrating before going to sleep on remembering in the morning what you did tonight. I shall not visit you again for at least a week, so you will have plenty of opportunity to experiment on your own and as I told you yesterday, if you get into any difficulty, I shall be near, to help you. Peace be with you, my son: I will leave you now.'

I could give a long description of the many incidents which took place the following week, but instead I shall summarize the highlights.

On the very first night I managed to make my way to Daphne's cottage where I found her entertaining friends. I was introduced to and had interesting conversations with several of them on current events in the world – on which topics I found them to be very well informed. Several movie films were shown for my benefit, depicting the gardens attached to the bungalows in this valley. These gardens were much more beautiful than any I had seen before. When gardens were shown which were not laid out in any way, I saw nature-spirits, tiny people who couldn't be much more than five to six inches high judging by comparison with the flowers I knew, dancing in and out of the pictures. When they lighted on a flower, the stem gave a slight tremor as it would if a large butterfly or bumble bee did the same thing. They are indeed perfect replicas of the fairies described in the books beloved by children of all ages – with one important difference, the complete absence of wings, and this can be understood, for logically wings are quite unnecessary at the level where these nature-spirits exist.

On the second night I got out of my body, meaning to visit the third sphere once more, but, when I found myself hovering immediately above the bed on which my body was lying, the first thing I heard was the voice of Charles speaking to me in characteristic army dialect. He said: 'It's about time you looked me up. I've been here at least three times since the night when you and your Indian friend came to London with me; each time your old body was here, but you had gone. I didn't know where you had pushed off to, so I couldn't follow you. This time I decided to come early so as to be sure to catch you.' 'My dear Charles,' I said, 'I'm terribly sorry. I didn't know you had been looking for me, for I have been exceedingly busy and very interested indeed in all that I have seen.' 'What about going up to your little turret room which I remember used to be a favourite of yours,' said Charles, 'then we can have a long talk, just like old times.' 'Good idea, old chap, let's go.' So we went up to my sanctum where we chatted over old days and I told him more or less everything that had happened to me up to date.

Charles said, 'I'm damned glad you've been so lucky as to meet Acharya for it worried me after I died to see how extremely depressed and miserable you were. I tried my damnedest to speak to you, but couldn't make you hear – we had been jolly good pals in the old days, even though I always looked on you as donkey's years older than me. I appreciate all you've done for me ever since the days when you started to teach me football, and gave me my first lesson in how to hold a bat. What a funny thing life is! My idea used to be more or less to have a good time and get the best out of life that I could, and possibly later to marry some nice girl and have a family. When I first met Acharya he impressed me with the fact that a man doesn't change after death, it is the conditions under which he lives that are different, and I have found that quite true.'

'Yes,' I replied, 'I gathered from Acharya that you had not been exactly miserable. He said you had linked up with some girl who had recently left the world. Is that so?'

Did he blush or was I imagining it? 'Yes, that's true enough,' said Charles, 'I think it passes the time to have a girl pal to wander round with. In her case I'm afraid it tickles my vanity, for she thinks I'm a hell of a fellow, just because I know a little more than she does. She didn't have a very good time in the world so I suppose this moving around, seeing shows and going to restaurants is thrilling for a time.' 'Oh, Charles,' I said, 'there's one thing I want to ask you. Is there any sex relationship at your level after you've dropped the physical body?' This time I'm quite sure he blushed, but he went on, 'Well yes, there is, of a kind, and I think most people indulge in it, but it's not quite the same thing as on the physical plane. One leads up to things in the same way, and although I would probably have felt just as shy about talking of my secret love affairs had you asked me the same question before I died, I suppose I feel just a wee bit shy of talking about these things now.'

I said, 'I didn't mean to be personal, I'm just interested in getting as much information as I can about the differences between conditions in the physical and the astral worlds and at various levels of the latter. I told you about my coming up against Daphne on one of the higher levels, where she is already studying music. I was very much in love with Daphne when she was alive and would have asked her to marry me as soon as I was able to support a wife. Although we never experienced the physical relationship of marriage, I feel that the platonic association we shall carry on now at these higher levels, will not only last through our astral existence but will be of great benefit to us in our next incarnation. What about coming along with me one night and letting me introduce you to Daphne?' 'Yes, I'd like to,' said Charles. I suggested a date for Thursday night, to which he agreed.

Charles said he had recently made contact with our father, who had died some years previously. From his description I gathered that father was living at the second sphere. Charles described how he had found him surrounded by rose bushes – this was as I had known him in my boyhood days – he said that the last time he had seen him, father was distressed because a Scotch terrier which had attached itself to him had suddenly disappeared and he felt it had been lost. I explained to Charles what had really happened, but he showed little interest. We talked on till a peculiar feeling of restlessness came over me. I had just time to say to Charles not to forget Thursday when I woke in my bed with no remembrance of how I got there.

It was on Wednesday night I had a most disturbing experience – a nightmare in which Daphne took part. It seemed that Daphne and I were in a dark cave. For some reason we could not escape from a loathsome gorilla-like creature who was seated on the floor close to us, glowering at Daphne who obviously attracted it in some horrible way. I know that in my dream I wanted to protect Daphne, but the gorilla was of such a size and strength that I knew I would have no chance against it. It seemed highly amused at our efforts to escape, for it emitted wild yells and hoarse laughter as we ran hither and thither around the cave, trying to find an exit. Even in my dream, sweat poured from my brow and I tried to think of Acharya in the hope he would come to our assistance – but nothing happened and we seemed left to our fate. After a little time the gorilla rose to its feet and advanced towards Daphne, whom it grasped with its horrible long hairy arms and commenced to drag her to the other end of the cave. Daphne screamed and resisted to the best of her ability, and in desperation I hurled myself at the horrible creature and, although I had no weapon, I endeavoured to get my hands on its throat, in the hope that it would turn its attentions to me. Even now, I can still smell the foetid breath of the brute, for in the middle of the fight I awoke in my bed, sweating profusely and with the bed-clothes all tangled about me. I haven't the slightest idea what it all means. I shall check up with Daphne as soon as possible in the hope she knows something about it.

Thursday was the night I began my career as an astral helper. This was the night on which I had arranged to take Charles to the third sphere. Charles was late, and when he arrived he was in an agitated condition because, he said, a pal of his, Bill Fletcher, had just crashed and been killed in a raid over London. He asked me to come with him and help, so we set out at once for London. Charles knew where to look for Bill and our assistance was welcomed by three inexperienced but eager astral helpers. After about two hours hard work on the part of all of us, Bill was persuaded to make the effort of will to free himself from his etheric body, and at once became quite a different person. Charles and I took charge of him; we went with him to his home where we did what we could to prepare his young wife for the news she would receive the following morning.

As Charles then undertook to remain with Bill, saying he knew only too well what the poor devil was suffering, I went back to the scene of the raid to see if I could be of any further assistance. An ambulance passed me, so I decided to follow it. It was driven to one of the big London hospitals and a stretcher, on which a young girl was lying, was carefully carried into the building. The same girl in her astral body was walking, in a very agitated condition, close beside the stretcher. After examination, the body of the girl was carried into one of the wards, already filled with recent casualties. Without any fuss or hurry and an efficiency at which I greatly marvelled, the girl was put to bed and arrangements were made for giving her a blood transfusion. She was frantically trying to communicate with the doctors and nurses attending to her unconscious body, but after a short time she listened to what I had to say. I told her she would be all right, for intuitively I knew this was so. I told her that it would help if she became calm and watched the proceedings, at the same time using her will-power to aid the efforts of the doctors and nurses. I don't know now, why I suggested this to her. I hadn't the slightest idea whether it would help or not, but it came to me to say this, and so I did.

I could see quite clearly that there was a thin line of etheric matter stretched between her astral body and physical form lying on the hospital bed, so I knew that she was not dead – and was sure she would not die. I stayed talking with her for the rest of my night, and after she had told me that the house in which she lived was next door to the one that had received a direct hit and that she was very worried indeed as to the fate of her old mother, began to give her a little of the knowledge which had recently been given to me.

There were other astral helpers moving about the ward and one of them whom I had not seen before but who said his name was Jim, congratulated me on my efforts, saying that he wished there were more people with the necessary knowledge who would help in similar emergencies.

I had an experience so unique during Friday night that I must describe the night's activities in some detail. I found Daphne in her room at the Academy. One of the first things I asked her about, was her part in my nightmare – but she assured me she was not present. We decided we would try to get to the next sphere – the fourth – on our own, but were faced with the problem that neither of us had a landmark there to visualize. We sat down outside and concentrated; I tried to see a mental hospital, such as Acharya had mentioned, but nothing happened. I wished we had Acharya to help us and must have made a thought-form of him because, after our next attempt had failed, I heard a chuckle behind me – and there he was. He said he would help us and give us landmarks on each sphere which we must memorize. We linked hands with him and when I opened my eyes, the scene that met them cannot adequately be described, for it was the most beautiful valley I have ever seen. It was partly wooded and the ground was covered with thick heather of the varied colours which one sees to perfection in South Africa, but soft to the touch; intermingled with this, wild flowers bloomed in profusion. Side by side I saw primroses, blue-bells, daffodils, forget-me-nots, tulips, wild roses and the most vivid red poppies that could be imagined; I'm sure no variety of wild flower was missing for the ground near and far was a veritable carpet of colours of breathtaking beauty. 'I thought you would be pleased with this landmark,' said Acharya, 'for it is called "The Fairy Glen". It could be described as the cradle of the deva kingdom for it is the valley to which the members of this evolution return after they have finished the particular work allotted to them. I suggest you both investigate the valley on some future occasion – quietly and unobtrusively, for the devas have their own methods of keeping away philistines amongst men. They build a thick wall of astral matter which makes it impossible for any human being to see beyond, even if they knew this place existed. Such walls serve the same purpose at this level as do brick walls in the physical world.'

Once more we joined hands and willed ourselves to the next level – the fifth. On opening my eyes it seemed uncanny to find that we were standing on an open plane like a desert, except that there was grass in the place of sand. In the distance was a huge city, with many spires and towers, surrounded by an immense wall. Above the city shone something in the nature of a sun, for it spread a glow over all the buildings which made them shine like gold. 'That, my friends, is the Golden City,' said our guide, 'and I advise you to visit and study it. You will find within everything that has ever been thought of or imagined as likely to be found in orthodox Heaven, so much talked of by priests and ministers attached to the Christian creed. The whole city is a huge thought-form and you will find therein thought-forms of God the Father, of Christ and his twelve disciples, and the many saints who have figured in the teachings of the Church.'

Again we linked hands, and willed ourselves to the sixth level. Within a second we were standing on the edge of a lake, which was surrounded by a high wall of rock. In the distance on our left was to be seen a very small opening – I wondered where it led. 'Make a clear picture of this scene,' advised Acharya. 'This lake is used principally by members of the human race who desire absolute silence for their particular work. There is one sect in the world which evolves entirely through meditation exercises. They are taught during their lifetime that there is this place, in rather the same way that Christians are taught that there is a place called Heaven. The small boats you see are used by the men who come here, for when they are afloat, it is impossible for one boat to be overtaken by another. This is due to some under water currents which cause the boats to drift round the entire lake; it takes twenty four hours (earth time) for a boat to return to its starting place, and the meditation exercises carried out by these people, take exactly that time to complete. I saw you noticed the small opening on the left; that leads to another similar but smaller lake, also surrounded by high cliffs. This lake was produced by an individual who sojourned here. One day he was interrupted in his meditations by other human beings using the lake at the same time as himself. The thought-form he made was so strong that he produced a lake all for himself. I have spoken to you here in a voice which is hardly above a whisper. Had I spoken in my usual voice you would have heard it reverberating round the lake like thunder. The people in the vicinity know about this unusual feature, and take good care never to make a sound. Because of this peculiarity the lake is called 'The Waters of Perpetual Silence'. Now I must leave you. You should find no difficulty in returning without my assistance.'

As he had surmised Daphne and I found no difficulty in retracing our steps, but when we reached the fourth sphere and once more saw the Fairy Glen, we decided to remain there for a short time. We noticed there were signs of great activity in the valley as if some sort of ceremony were about to take place. There seemed to be thousands of inhabitants gathering in the valley. We sat down to watch; our presence was noticed by some 'officials' and when one of them moved towards us, we rather expected to be asked to go away – particularly as Acharya had warned us that members of our evolution were not always welcome here. The man who, slowly and in a dignified manner, floated towards us had a very fine intellectual head and a spiritual dignity which made us rise to our feet instinctively as he reached us. His costume was strange to us, it resembled that of a Chinese Mandarin. The colours of the long coat were exquisite, whilst the embroidery clearly portrayed many of the wild flowers that bloomed in the valley. The expression on his face did not seem to auger trouble for us, so we smiled in return, hoping that our attitude would reassure him. What followed was a little uncanny for it was a conversation conducted without a word being uttered; question and answer followed one upon the other, far more quickly than would have been possible had words been our medium of expression.

I felt he had asked me whether he could do anything for us. I told him, merely by allowing the thought to express itself in my mind, that Daphne was a permanent inhabitant of the astral world, whereas I was still living in a physical body in the world and was here during the period when my body was sleeping. He seemed to understand perfectly, and said he had been instructed by his 'Chief' to bring us to him. We intimated that we were only too willing to accompany him and at once moved towards the central arena. As we approached, I saw that the people were standing and sitting around a large open circle. Wild flowers had been strung together to keep back the crowds and I could not help comparing the beauty of that 'fence' with those we see in the world. Just within the circle a dais had been erected, made entirely of great clumps of green moss with pillars at each corner, formed of intertwined flowers of every size and colour; even the awning above the dais was made of a very delicate fern, not unlike our maiden-hair variety. The whole formed a most beautiful picture. The moss on the floor of the dais had been laid in such a way, that there appeared to be numerous seats with shaped backs, which looked so comfortable that one immediately wished to sit down. At the front there were two large seats, almost like thrones, and, although these too were composed of moss, they were more ornate than the others.

Whilst we waited for the 'Chief' to appear, our guide told us something of what was about to take place. The gist of what he said was that the crowd had gathered together to witness a graduation ceremony. He explained that when the time came for a group of nature-spirits to pass to the next stage in their evolution, which was to become devas, they had to give proof of their proficiency at one of these gatherings. Providing they satisfied a 'Council of Examiners', they were changed from nature-spirits into devas, with more responsible duties. He said that the younger egos evolved along one of three special lines of work: (1) the Power line, working through Music and Colour; (2) the guidance of the Vegetable Kingdom, which derived its change and progress from experiments made at the astral level by members of the deva evolution, and (3) work in connection with the Human Kingdom. He explained that the nature-spirits mixed quite frequently with human beings, particularly children. They often played with those who came to the astral world at an early age and taught them how to make use of the plastic astral matter, so as to live their fairy stories in very truth, by changing at will so as to represent any figure of fiction for so long as required and so long as the thoughts of those taking part lasted. It was impressed on me that this sphere of the astral world is for the deva kingdom what the physical world is for the human kingdom. Between lives, birds return to this fourth sphere, in the same way that animals inhabit the sixth and seventh spheres, when they are awaiting their return to the world. Birds, as well as fish, butterflies and many other winged creatures, eventually change into nature-spirits and are part of the deva evolution. They never become part of our human evolution.

At this stage a group emerged from a nearby coppice. If ever I had imagined the fairy story of the 'Magic Carpet' come to life, surely this was it! The group consisted of two central figures, both seated cross-legged on what can only be described as a ceremonial carpet, floating about a yard above the ground. From each front corner, strands of flowers were held in the beaks of numerous birds of every colour imaginable, and whilst these flew ahead, seemingly pulling the carpet along, the other devas taking part in the procession floated majestically on either side of it. More little birds flew backwards and forwards, dropping rose petals in the path of the procession, each bird swooping down to the ground, picking a petal with its beak from the rose bushes that grew everywhere, and at once returning to its position ahead of the procession, from where the petal was dropped. Whilst the procession slowly wended its way, the air was filled with the notes issuing from the throats of thousands of birds of all types. The procession reached its destination and the two central figures were escorted to the special thrones prepared for them on the dais. The first of the two figures was the 'Chief' and the second the High Priest, judging from the ceremonial robes that he wore. As the other officials took their place on the dais, our guide presented Daphne and me to the Chief who intimated that we were to seat ourselves on the platform. Daphne was offered a seat at his right hand and I was given a seat to the immediate left of the High Priest. Before the ceremony proper commenced, some music was played by a large orchestra, composed entirely of devas, it was of an extremely cheerful and melodious character. After the orchestra had finished playing, there was silence again; even the myriads of birds uttered no sound whatever.

A herald then entered the inner circle and with a small silver trumpet proclaimed the first part of the ceremony. A small group of nature-spirits came into the arena. Although no words were spoken, a question passed from the principal examiner to this group. It related to the expression of sounds, as representing a slowly moving river, lazily passing through wooded country with tall trees on either side of the river bank. At once the group produced wind instruments and a curious sort of guitar. They commenced to play and I saw the thought-form slowly take shape, showing exactly what they were endeavouring to illustrate through sound. This was immediately followed by another order to produce music that expressed the elements. At once the instruments were changed;

several drums, one set of cymbals and two other larger and quite unusual wind instruments, rather like oboes, were introduced. Again they played and it was not difficult to realize, even without looking at the thought-form so clearly outlined before us, that a storm at sea was the subject of the theme then played. One could almost hear the creaking of the stays and halyards, strained to their utmost by the force of the gale. Thunder and lightning played their part and as this group finished, the crowd stood up as a body, raising their hands to the sky, instead of clapping and cheering as we would do. That was all the first group was asked to do and I was sure the members had successfully passed their test.

The second group was now heralded into the circle – there were only five of them. They were asked to demonstrate the result of certain graftings, as related to both flowers and shrubs and to different kinds of fruit. The answers appeared immediately as thought-form pictures, showing very clearly the changes in size and colour. They were also asked what kinds of flowers could be grown together in one bed and which kinds meant death to one or more of the species. Then questions concerning crop rotation and why it was necessary. This second group also seemed to satisfy both examiners and crowd.

The silver trumpet sounded again and the third group of very small nature-spirits then entered the circle and thought-forms of three human children were created by the examiners. They were typical fair-haired English children of an age between five and seven. They discussed the fairy story of Cinderella. At once they were joined by the nature-spirits who entered into the spirit of the game. They argued as to who should take the principal part and when this was settled I noticed that the nature-spirits took over the parts that children usually object to play – they became the ugly sisters, and the unpleasant father, leaving the parts of Cinderella, the Fairy Godmother and the Prince for the children. A short version of the play was enacted, but the transformation scenes covering the fairy carriage and the change of Cinderella's clothes were much more realistic than anything that has ever been produced under physical plane conditions. I imagine the unselfishness shown by the little nature-spirits made the difference between passing or failing the test.

After a short interval, with cheerful music, all the members of the three groups who had been examined were called back into the arena. The herald sounded the entrance on his silver trumpet. The examiners grouped round the Chief and High Priest then drew together, as if to confer on what they had seen, and after a few moments the chief examiner stood before the Chief and obtained his consent for the nature-spirits to be promoted to deva rank.

The High Priest then rose to his feet, bowed to the Chief and solemnly walked into the arena where the nature-spirits were standing. For the first time words were used. The High Priest, raising his hands above his head, intoned an invocation in the same unknown language I had heard in the glade on the third sphere. The herald then handed him a large sword, the blade of which shone brightly in the clear astral light. Raising it towards the sky, he uttered more words and slowly walked towards the first of the nature-spirits, who stood in one long line in front of him. He placed the sword on the head of the first and said two words which seemed to mean 'God go with thee' (though why I thought this, I do not know) and as I watched, the form of the nature-spirit which had appeared to be that of a little old man, changed to that of a young girl. The same thing happened to all the graduates. Some male nature-spirits became male devas, whereas others changed their sex. All the newly created bodies were young in appearance.

I was about to thank the Chief for the wonderful opportunity offered to us when, without any warning, I felt my body calling me and I found myself awake in bed in Colombo.

On the following Saturday night when I got out of my body, I found Jim, the astral helper I had met in the London hospital, waiting for me. He had come to ask for my help. He stated that he had been very impressed by the way in which I had handled the case of the girl – whose name was Mary – on Thursday night, and felt I could give further help. This girl had learned from a thoughtless visitor that her mother had been killed in the raid and was so upset that no one could do anything with her. As there was a young sister, Irene, aged seven, it would be a tragedy if Mary died too. I was only too glad to have this opportunity of putting into practice what I had recently learned. When we reached the ward, I saw Mary's fever-racked body tossing on the bed, whilst the girl herself was pacing the ward, metaphorically tearing her hair. She welcomed my arrival, and as I talked soothingly to her, quietened down. I made a thought-form of a comfortable settee and whilst we sat there I gave her what help I could from the knowledge which had been given me by Acharya. I brought the conversation round to Irene and pointed out how she would suffer if both her mother and sister died. I assured Mary – with an authority I did not possess – that she could live, if she made the effort, and if she elected to do so she would still be able to contact her mother during sleep. She asked me if I would help her. I promised to do so and thus took on myself a measure of responsibility. I said I would return the following night.

On the Sunday night Mary was waiting for me and was quite calm. I suggested we look for her mother. I showed her how easy it was to travel under astral conditions and soon this method of progress both interested and intrigued her. She took me to the block of flats where they lived. We found Irene in a neighbour's flat, and by her bedside her mother was sitting endeavouring to comfort the weeping child who could not see her. At first the mother thought Mary was dead too, but when she realized this was not the case and that she would be able to care for Irene, she calmed down. I left the three of them to chat and, after arranging to meet them there later, returned to the hospital. I watched Jim and his colleagues working, and made notes of their methods. When Mary, her mother and Irene came in, I spent the rest of my night trying to help them in the way Acharya had helped me. The mother was not a very highly evolved person – I had learned from an astral helper that it had taken two days to persuade her to make the effort of will to disconnect herself from her etheric body. At last she seemed to grasp the link with her family was not broken and that she would still see them at night.

This made her much happier. I fancy she will be quite content with first sphere conditions for some time. My last act before returning to my body was to use what will-power I possess to impress upon Irene that when she awakened she must remember something of what she had been told during her sleep.

CHAPTER TEN

Acharya arrived on the stroke of 11 o'clock, as I had expected he would. First of all, he asked me to give him the record of my experiences during the past week. He read through this very carefully before commencing to speak. As he read, his expression showed more and more his appreciation of my efforts so I was not at all surprised when he said: 'I must really congratulate you on all that you have done during the past seven nights. My leaving you to work on your own at this early stage of your training was a gamble, but the results have proved that I was not wrong in thinking that you were ready to take over a little responsibility, even though your tuition had lasted such a relatively short time. I am indeed happy that I was chosen as an instrument to alleviate the distress which was exceedingly apparent when we first met.

'There is very little that requires comment in your experiences of last Monday night. A coloured movie film is frequently utilized by permanent inhabitants of the astral world for the purpose of displaying pictures of particular places they wish to show to their friends so that they need not burden their memories unduly with the scenes they wish to show. To use the astral counterpart of a photographic film is an even simpler method and providing the operator has brought over with him the technical knowledge, the results are identical with what a similar show would be in the world.

'I am satisfied that you realize it is extremely unlikely that Charles will want to leave the part of the astral plane in which he is now living, for a considerable time.

'Then there is your experience of Wednesday night, when all that you remembered took the form of a nightmare. You have already inquired from Daphne, whether she had any recollection of taking part in your dream and she has assured you that, so far as she is aware, she did not have any part in it – and you can rest assured this statement is correct, for there are no periods in her life in the astral world when she loses consciousness and so would not be sure of what she had done. In order that you may understand my explanation of this occurrence, I want you to take your mind back to a previous talk. In it I told you that the perfected men or Masters give instruction to pupils in certain circumstances. I shall give you a very brief outline of the work of these pupils. There are two grades of pupils, one called Probationary and the other Accepted. The only difference between the two is, that once a pupil has been accepted by a Master, he is, as it were, taken on the permanent staff and utilized for this work not only in his present life but both after death and in lives that are to come. A probationary pupil is tried out, and only after he has served in that capacity possibly several lives is he taken into the very much closer touch with the Master that one finds with accepted pupils. At no time is any compulsion used, for even the Masters have no authority to interfere with the free will which is given to every man at the moment of individualization, but before a human being can be utilized for occult work by these great Beings, he must show that he has eradicated completely the emotion of *fear* from his make up and must prove that at all times he is willing to *sacrifice* himself in the interest of the work. It is necessary for the student to pass five astral tests – these are usually remembered by him in the form of dreams or nightmares. I have been given authority to tell you, that your determination to overcome the difficulties of understanding astral plane conditions has been noticed by one of these Masters and it is possible that, in the fullness of time, you will be given the opportunity of serving the White Brotherhood, to which He belongs – this means that you will probably be taken on as a probationary pupil. The dream you had on Wednesday night was actually an astral test – through which you passed quite successfully. The test was to prove that, although obviously you were frightened by the gorilla-like creature, actually a thought-form created by the Master concerned, yet you were willing to forget yourself and if necessary make the supreme sacrifice, in order to protect what was only a thought-form of Daphne, but which was an intense reality to you. Had you refused to make an effort to save her, you would have returned to your body a little earlier than you actually did with the same memory of a nightmare but in that case you would have failed and proved to the Master, who was watching you at the time, that you were unsuitable and insufficiently advanced in evolution for the purpose he had in mind. In the course of the next few years you will probably find that you remember further dreams, these will be more astral tests, all of which you must pass before you can qualify for the work proposed for you. As a personality you know very little about such things, but the real you, the ego, knows perfectly well what is happening and he, I happen to know, is very keen indeed to make the grade and be used for the helping of humanity.

'Because of the interest you have shown in the instruction I have given you, I shall give you a rough idea of what you have to accomplish, before you can qualify for this special work. You have to know how to move about quickly and effectively on all the different planes of the astral world. You have to know all about the lower astral entities, including those which have etheric bodies – such as the elementals you saw at the bottom of the sea – and must be trained so that the hypnotic effect of the eyes of such creatures has no effect on you. There is a fire test, taking the shape of a fierce forest fire, which you must walk through without fear and with unhurried steps. This sounds easy but it is not quite so easy at the time. The terrific heat, which you feel in your astral body in the same way that a physical fire of similar dimensions would be felt, is likely to terrify you and make you think that you would be destroyed if you attempted to pass through it. Once you realize that because you are in your astral body you cannot be harmed, you calmly walk through the fire and the test has been passed. There is a water test which teaches you to travel under the sea, and you would be surprised at the number of students who fail that. They succumb to a feeling of suffocation, due entirely to imagination but which nevertheless produces fear; this drives them back to their physical bodies and they awake, realizing that they have had a bad dream. You have to satisfy the Master who is interested in you that you can differentiate between a permanent inhabitant of the astral world and one who is sojourning there during a sleep period. You must prove that you have developed the sympathetic understanding which enables you to work in conjunction with the members of the deva evolution – co-operation with them is often necessary in this work. You must be able to tell the difference between a thought-form of a particular person and the man himself, for if a Master were to send you with a message to be delivered to someone living in a different sphere of the astral world from that in which he was functioning at the moment, you might be accosted by an entity who was antagonistic to that Master and who, for the purpose of deceiving you, had taken the appearance of the individual you were seeking (really a thought-form made in his likeness) you might deliver the message to this man thinking he was the real person; this might have serious repercussions on the work the Master was doing at the time. Such impersonations are very common in the astral world and you have to be trained to use certain power signs, which enable you to prove conclusively whether the person concerned is genuine or not. You have probably heard of vampires. They do exist but fortunately are uncommon. They live under similar conditions to suicides; both are earthbound, and you must know not only how to help them, but how to release them from their bondage. I think I have told you sufficient to show that you still have much to learn.

'I shall now pass on to your Friday night's adventure when you found some difficulty in passing to the higher levels without having any focal points there on which to concentrate. I was keeping in touch with you mentally, as I thought you would probably make some such attempt on one of the nights when I left you free to experiment alone. As you found out, it is quite simple to get to any part of the astral world, providing you have a special landmark to use for that purpose. I do not expect I shall find it necessary to come to your assistance again in the future. I did not give you a focal point on the seventh sphere, for there is little there that would interest you, and it is not desirable for you to come into unnecessary contact with the shells existing at that level at present.

'You were indeed very fortunate to have the opportunity of witnessing the graduation ceremony (as I note you call it) in which certain nature-spirits were changed into junior members of the deva kingdom. Nature-spirits are of course part of the deva evolution although there is a tremendous difference between a nature-spirit and a deva. It is not possible to give you a parallel example in your evolution. Very few people, whether living in the astral or the physical world, have had the privilege of seeing what you saw the other night and I am exceedingly glad that on your return journey from higher levels you stopped for a short time at the fourth sphere.

'I had no hand in making the opportunity for you to put into practice some of the teaching I have been privileged to give you in your experiences on Saturday and Sunday nights, therefore I can say without hesitation, that your work was not only extremely valuable, but very well done indeed. In offering to pass on some of the knowledge you have to the girl Mary, you have of course taken on certain responsibilities, also it is more than likely that the astral helper whom you refer to as Jim, will ask you again to help him, whenever his organization is overworked; this will not only give you great opportunities for service, which always makes for good karma, but you will find that your interest in and understanding of your fellow human beings will increase a thousand-fold from this work. The technique you employed in connection with the girl Mary and her family was in every way correct. You must not be disappointed if Mary does not react to your tuition and prove as proficient a pupil as I have found you to be, for as I have told you repeatedly, it is the *intention* which matters and not the result. Your efforts to will that the child Irene should remember on awakening something of what you told her during sleep were entirely successful, and today she is feeling quite different about the loss she has sustained. I leave it to you to decide when you consider it necessary to visit the family again, for they are now your responsibility and will only be taken up by others should you fail to give them the assistance that, of your own free will, you have promised.

'I shall now talk to you about the mental world. I told you that after a period of time it became necessary for all of us to drop our astral bodies and leave the astral for the mental world. The period of time varies according to our stage in evolution: a man who has had about fifty lives will spend much longer in the astral world and shorter in the mental than will one who has lived five hundred lives in different bodies and in environments where he has had opportunities for intellectual pursuits. In one of my talks I compared the bodies we function in to a man dressed in underclothes, a suit of clothes and an overcoat. When death occurs at the physical level, this corresponds to dropping the overcoat (the physical body), when it occurs at the astral level, it corresponds to dropping the suit of clothes (the astral body), this leaves the man garbed in his underclothes (the mental body) and it is in this vehicle that he enters the mental world.

'As I have said, the mental body is the first body the ego draws round him in his descent from the causal level. It is fashioned of even finer material than the astral. Actually, it is the thought-form of the individual. As you could not yet comprehend a description of this wispy, cloudy form which appears to lack all density, I shall only give you a physical comparison of the mental body of an unevolved human being, say one who has had about fifty incarnations, with that of an evolving human being, say one who has had about five hundred incarnations, by likening them to a wicker basket as seen in two stages of the making – the early stage and the more finished article. In the early stages you see a basket take shape but it has only a few strands of cane fixed to its base. Eventually all the gaps are filled in and the finished article is blended together of many hundreds of wicker strands all separate and distinct from each other but appearing at first sight to be a composite whole. Each of these strands may be thought of as representing a particular subject of mental development which has been more or less mastered by that individual.

'When a person has finished his life in the astral world, he passes to the seventh sphere of that world; when it is time for him to move on from there, he becomes sleepy, loses consciousness, and awakens almost immediately in the mental world. When, after his physical death, a man becomes fully conscious in the astral world, his first sensation is a feeling of well-being and buoyant health. When, after his astral death, he becomes fully conscious in the mental world, his first sensation is that of profound bliss and a feeling of being at peace with mankind. In the early stages he may not even realize that he has passed to the mental plane, for he feels so contented and happy there that he is willing to let well alone for the time being. In due course he realizes the change in his surroundings and once more he has to be taught, by those who wait to welcome him, the difference between the conditions under which he must now live and those relating to the world he has just left.

'The mental world is the world of thought. Thoughts are the only realities; they *are* things just as much as chairs and tables are things, only – in the same way that the mental body is composed of finer material than the physical – they too are composed of finer matter. It is quite impossible to do so, but if we could take any of our astral or physical matter into the world of thought, it would not exist for the people there. Such things would be more or less the same as thought-forms in the physical world; they surround us all the time but we cannot see them – although they influence our minds. My greatest difficulty in explaining to you what conditions are like in the mental world is that there are no words which enable us to describe in detail conditions of consciousness which are entirely foreign to physical plane understanding. At the mental level you do not see other people as individuals, nor as astral counterparts of physical forms, but as thought-forms of the individual concerned, and these thought-forms accord with the mental development of the individual.

'A man functioning at the mental level can be likened to a wireless set, that both receives and transmits. The number of wave lengths which he can use in receiving and transmitting depends entirely upon the number of subjects with which such a man is familiar. He can receive on his set the thoughts of others providing he can tune-in to that particular wave length – in other words if he has some knowledge of the subject of which the thought is composed – and he can carry on a conversation on that subject, because he himself can answer the thought-forms that he receives by transmission of his own thoughts, which would then be picked up by all other people having similar knowledge and interests.

'At the astral level you saw the intellectual giants creating beautiful music, pictures etc., and teaching others in the arts and sciences. When they pass from the astral to the mental world, they continue to help others who are treading the path which they have trod; but at the mental level their tuition takes the form of technical and theoretical lectures sent out in a perpetual stream of thought. All of these can be picked up by anyone interested in the same subject. You can only grasp as much of the thoughts as by your own intellectual activities of the past you are able to comprehend. The parts of the thoughts which are beyond your understanding do not register at all and are not picked up by you, for your receiving set is limited to your understanding; if you had never studied such subjects as mathematics or chemistry, you would not be able to respond to the thoughts of them that might be all round you, given out by people who are well versed in these particular sciences. At the mental level the life is much more interesting for an intellectual man than for one of limited intelligence. Take the case of a person who, during his lifetime, has made a study of one particular subject; here he would come in contact with other intellectuals who were masters of his subject, merely through sensing and seeing the thought-forms expressed by them there. Because he was no longer limited by an inadequate brain, he would understand quite clearly not only all the things which he understood perfectly at the physical level, but the many things which in his physical life he was only able to realize in principle and not grasp completely.

'A man continues his mental development for a considerable time, not only to his great satisfaction but also to his great benefit in future lives as, through and because of the work he has done, he has earned the right to be given in his next physical incarnation a brain which will fully comprehend the knowledge which he consolidated during his stay in the mental world. When I tell you that men of highly developed intellects have been known to spend as much as two and three thousand years at the mental level, you will perhaps admit that for such people life could not be considered dull. On the other hand the time that an unevolved being spends at this level is usually very short indeed, for he has little to consolidate and certainly his life there is not nearly as pleasant or as interesting as the lives of his more intellectual brethren. He does not realize his limitations so there is no suffering whatever, even for the man of the most limited intelligence that you can visualize. When the egos who have been existing in the Golden City pass to the mental world they still have only one cardinal thought in their minds and that is their idea of *Heaven*. Their religious teachers have taught them that once they have been "received into heaven", they are there for ever. They are quite sure that they have been so received, for they have been living under the conditions which to them are in accordance with the promises of eternal bliss, to which they have looked forward. They expect to remain permanently in a heaven world and, because of this dominating belief, the illusion of heaven, as they have always imagined it, is created by them, in it they live, exchanging their thoughts with the thoughts of others, sent out by people who are controlled by the same illusions. Thus the whole of their mental life is lived within a gigantic thought-form. Although they are perfectly happy they do not usually benefit as much from these conditions as others who use the mental world, not only for consolidating their own mental activities but also, for adding to the intellectual knowledge which they possessed before reaching that sphere of consciousness. The people who live surrounded by their idea of heaven are radiantly happy and perfectly content, so who is to say that they are worse off than others who travel by different paths.

'In the mental world there are again seven spheres of consciousness corresponding to those found at the astral level, but in this world there is no difficulty at all in passing from one sphere to another – whether you go up or down. In practice, however, you will find that the permanent inhabitants move about very little indeed. The average man finds his natural home, that is the sphere most suited to him and in which he will be most happy, on any of the first four spheres. Only the outstandingly intellectual individuals go beyond the fourth sphere. Usually a man who passes from the astral to the mental world, aided by those helpers who meet him, finds his way almost at once to the particular sphere of consciousness that applies to his mental development, and there he stays, until the time comes for him to drop his mental body and spend a short time at the causal level, which is the permanent home of the ego.

'Before I talk to you much more on this subject, I propose to take you on Wednesday night as far as the second sphere of the mental world, in order that you may get a clearer understanding of what I am now trying to tell you. You will then not only realize my present difficulties, but will probably find that if you try to report your activities on that journey, there are no adequate words to express what you saw there. I shall visit you again on Friday morning, this will leave you three nights in which to continue your experiments in the astral world, although I advise you very strongly not to set out with any specific intention tonight, but to give your brain a rest. Reserve Wednesday night for me.' Acharya then left the room and I remained seated at my desk rather dazed with all this new information.

The first night I slept peacefully and woke much refreshed – with no remembrance of anything that had taken place during the night.

The following night I managed to reach Daphne quite easily. She had found no difficulty in returning to her cottage from the Fairy Glen – so presumably she has developed sufficient will-power to enable her to move freely from sphere to sphere. She told me that after I had left, an unbelievably beautiful exhibition of dancing had taken place in which the devas, the nature-spirits and even the birds took part. When she made adieus to the Chief, he told her we were welcome to re-visit the valley at any time.

I asked if she would be interested in seeing the Golden City at close quarters. As she was delighted with the idea, we there and then linked hands and reached the landmark for the fifth sphere in a very short time – having stopped en route at the Fairy Glen. The heavy gates which appeared to be made of gold were closed, but were unlocked and opened to us by an old gentleman who might have passed for the mythical St. Peter; he asked our business, we explained who we were and indicated that curiosity was the main object of our visit. He did not seem to mind this and offered a guide to show us round.

The streets seemed to be paved with pure gold, the numerous trees which lined them were laden with precious stones. These thought-forms of diamonds, emeralds, rubies, pearls etc. were very beautiful, but the effect was rather like an unending line of Christmas trees. I noticed that there was at least one church in every street; we were taken into what the guide stated was one of the smallest Roman Catholic churches. The sanctuary was a very beautiful piece of architecture, whilst the main altar might have been carved out of a gigantic pearl; a musician who was playing the organ was no ordinary exponent of the art. The guide invited us to visit churches of other denominations. I asked whether the different denominations kept themselves separate. He told me that in the Heaven world the different sects led their separate lives and carried out their specific teaching, but that there was never any disharmony here, everyone realized that the truth behind all doctrines was the same and only the forms of expression were different. In reply to a question I put, he stated that here God reigned supreme and from time to time visited the Golden City; He was not seen by the ordinary inhabitants, but His voice was heard seemingly coming from the cloud which encircled Him. He stated that Christ and His twelve apostles still walked the streets teaching, and preaching to the multitude. I asked if he had not meant eleven apostles, for surely Judas would not be admitted to the Heaven world. He assured me however that as Judas had paid the penalty of his crime by suffering terrible remorse and creating for himself a veritable hell, his repentance had been noted and he had been allowed to rejoin his fellow disciples. We visited an amphitheatre where there must have been three thousand people gathered together, all wearing white robes, listening to a choir singing to the accompaniment of harps and a silver toned organ; they had the appearance of the angels of the scriptures, but we did not see any seated on clouds playing harps.

We returned to Daphne's cottage where we discussed our experiences and later I met some more of her friends.

On Wednesday evening I was waiting for Acharya when he arrived in my room on the stroke of 10 p.m. Greeting me with 'If you are ready, let's be on our way,' we started off.

We travelled by the same route as before, via the village on the second sphere, the Academy on the third, the Fairy Glen on the fourth, the Golden City on the fifth and the lake on the sixth. At this last spot I had time to see that two of the little boats were in use, one on the opposite side of the lake, and the second near the opening to the small lake. I had to look for some time before I could see any motion at all, so slowly did they move. This is indeed an ideal spot for a man desiring solitude. As I had not yet visited the seventh sphere and had no focal point on which to concentrate, Acharya told me to hold his hand. When our surroundings became clear again I saw we were standing on the highest point of a range of mountains which Acharya stated was called 'World's View' – from here people would take a look at the surrounding world which must last them until their next incarnation. Although the countryside was reasonably well wooded with plenty of flowers in bloom, there were no buildings anywhere and the surroundings had a bleak appearance. I was told that a number of ascetics and holy men spend a large part of their lives under these conditions; I felt pleased that mysticism was not the line which appealed to me. I noticed two people who looked like a man and a woman gently floating along a valley. Upon asking Acharya who they were, he replied: 'Let us go and see.' We floated towards them. When we reached them they did not slow their progress, which was little faster than a walking pace, and when Acharya spoke to them they made no reply. I too put a question to the woman who turned her face in my direction but looked through me without uttering a word; her eyes had a blank stare and the face expressed no animation. They floated along on a route which appeared to be circular. My guide told me these were shells left behind by two individuals who had passed to the mental world.

Acharya now explained that in order to travel to the mental world we must leave our astral vehicles behind. To ensure that they were properly looked after and not taken possession of by astral entities, he proposed to leave them in the charge of two of his friends whom he could trust. He concentrated deeply and after about a minute told me they were on their way. Almost at once two European men of highly intellectual and spiritual appearance floated towards us. After greetings had been exchanged, Acharya told them what he wished them to do. I was then told to lie flat on my back with my hands folded beneath my head; Acharya took up a similar attitude but allowed his right hand to rest on my forehead. He told me to relax and to endeavour to make my mind a blank.

As Acharya predicted, I am finding it almost impossible to describe in words what the mental world is like. It seemed as if two or three minutes elapsed from the time I was told to relax until I realized that Acharya was talking to me, although he was not using words nor making any sounds whatever. I opened my eyes and found that an amazing stillness prevailed; we seemed to be suspended in space, but we were surrounded by all sorts of misty objects, which might or might not have been buildings, landscapes or people. Some of these objects were coloured, but nothing seemed to be very distinct; all of them, even the forms which might have been men, seemed to be changing all the time. I did not actually see them with my eyes, but sensed them in a way which was quite different from anything I had experienced before. I could see the thought-forms that were floating behind me as well as I could see those which were in front of me, thus I did not find it necessary to turn round and face a particular picture in order to see what it was like. It was all very uncanny, and I would perhaps have felt a trifle frightened had I not been in such excellent company. All this time Acharya was sending out thoughts to me, which I received just as clearly as if he had been speaking, and it was obvious that he had received my replies as soon as I had expressed them in my mind. He told me that this was the lowest sphere of the mental world and that it was inhabited mostly by entities of a very low mental development. He pointed out the thought-forms of several people who were living at this level. They were wispy creatures without any apparent solidity; many could hardly be described as concrete forms at all, for they were little more than smoke or cloud that appeared to take human form, but owing to its lack of density did not retain the same outline for any length of time. I have seen similar shapes take form when watching smoke coming from a fire, which almost instantly vanishes up the chimney. Under these mental plane conditions Acharya appeared to be a much bigger person than in either the astral or physical worlds, and he appeared clearer cut and much more solid in form than any of the other entities whose forms floated across my vision. His appearance in these surroundings enabled me to appreciate his comparison of the mental body of a man low in evolution, and that of one more evolved, to a wicker basket in the making and the same when completed.

Acharya told me to come close to him; he placed his hand on my shoulder – although I felt no touch – and said we were now passing to the second sphere. Without any sense of movement such as I had previously experienced, the scene changed in the same way as it does on a cinema screen. Our new surroundings were not very different from those we had left, with the exception that the forms which floated about had a clearer outline.

Acharya asked me to choose a subject on which I would like to have a discussion with one of the permanent inhabitants, and told me to send out thought-forms into the ether asking anyone who was interested in this subject to get in touch with me. Without thinking very much, I chose the subject of comparative religions. Immediately, through the medium of thought-forms, the reply came back in the form of a query as to what religion I belonged to. My thought passed back that I was a Roman Catholic, though not a strict one. The thought which returned was that all religions had their uses, in that they enabled people who could not stand alone to have something on which to lean, and in most cases they acted as a guide in the decisions which they had to make during their lifetimes. He stated that each religion had been started for a specific purpose, but that basically the truths of all were the same.

This thought asserted that the keynote of the Christian religion was *love*, and in accordance with its philosophy man could only evolve through loving his fellow man and by being *tolerant* of other men's opinions and actions. The religion started by the Lord Buddha was just as fine a philosophy as that preached by the Christ – the keynote of Buddhism was *wisdom*, and according to its teachings the most important thing in life is to act according to the *law of karma* through which men suffered or received benefits according to their actions, thoughts or words. The tendency of this religion is to eliminate emotion. The great religion known as Hinduism, which was revived Shri Krishna nearly two thousand years ago, had as its keynote *cleanliness* and *orderly conduct* – its orthodox members carried out special ablutions at stated intervals. Islam, founded by Mahomet, has as its keynote *courage* – its followers certainly did not lack that particular virtue. Zoroastrianism, the religion of the Parsees, had gradually been evolved through the many incarnations of Zoroaster. Fire was its sacred symbol and as fire has always been considered a purifier, the keynote of this religion is *purity*. Members even went so far as to say that fire must not be desecrated to light a cigarette or a pipe. He criticized proselytising in any form and urged me never to try to change a man's faith unless I were perfectly sure that man was seeking for something new and had lost interest in the religion into which he had been born. He said he could never understand an atheist, for no one could be *sure* that there were neither past nor future lives, but he sympathized with agnostics who were honest people, and only too willing to be convinced if arguments could be found to satisfy them. The pity was that they did not realize that most religious doctrines which concerned non-physical conditions, could never be proved by physical plane experiment.

I would have liked to have carried on with other subjects, but my guide told me to end the conversation, as I had had sufficient for one night and probably much more than I could retain in physical consciousness.

I asked if there was no music at this level. Acharya replied by asking which was my favourite symphony. I said I thought it was Beethoven's Choral Symphony, the Ninth. He said: 'Make a thought-form of the movement you like best and you will probably have a surprise.' Naturally I thought of the beautiful choral movement and, even as I thought, I heard the music which I loved so well, seemingly coming from all around us. I listened, enthralled, until it finished with the final notes of that beautiful work. I do not think I shall ever forget this – the performance was finer in every way than anything that could be imagined under world conditions; the purity of the voices and the perfection of the playing were beyond anything I had ever conceived as possible.

Acharya told me it was no use trying to remember any focal point, as it would be quite impossible for me to visit the mental world again at my present stage of development. We set about our return journey in the same way as when we came, and after a moment I seemed to wake up in my astral body, still lying in the position in which I had left it, with the two astral helpers 'on guard'. Both smiled at the consternation on my face, but I still felt exceedingly bewildered by what I had seen. They took leave of us both by bowing politely and moving into the distance. Shortly after, I woke in my bedroom to find that it was 3.15 a.m. I got up and recorded what was still clear in my mind.

On the following night before going to sleep, I decided that I would see how Mary was progressing but, when I got out of my body, I found Charles in my room. He had no plans to suggest, so I asked him if he would care to come with me to the London hospital ward – thinking the experience would be helpful for him. He agreed and we set off. Reaching the ward, we found Mary wide awake. I tentatively suggested to Charles that until she was out of her body, we might go to the third sphere and visit Daphne – the proposition had no interest for him at all, so we wandered round the wards till, on our next visit, we found Mary had gone to sleep and disconnected herself from her body.

Mary told me that things had been much better for her since she had seen me last and that Irene had remembered more than she did of what I had said on that occasion. Mary was spending her nights in her old home with her mother and sister, but did not remember much of what took place. I gave her as many hints as I could, taking my own case as a guide. I told her if at any time in the future she wished for my help, to think strongly about me, and I would endeavour to respond.

Charles' only comment on the incident was that Mary was a very pretty girl! He suggested putting in the rest of the night by taking me for a 'flip' as he had always looked forward to showing me that in one thing at least he had much more experience than I had. I agreed; whereupon he produced a thought-form of a two-seater Pussmoth type of 'plane, in which he piloted me all over Australia explaining the mechanism of the 'plane by the way. While still over that continent I felt the now familiar call and leaving the 'plane in full flight found myself back in my body in Colombo.

CHAPTER ELEVEN

Acharya arrived ten minutes earlier than usual, whilst I was still finishing my breakfast. It had taken me a considerable time to type out the details of what had happened during the week and I had not dared either to shave or have my bath before finishing that work, in case my memory of last night's activities dimmed and part of it would be lost. He did not seem to mind that I was not quite ready for him; he apologized for being early, seated himself upon the carpet in his usual place and asked me if he might read through the notes that I had made. I handed him the typed pages which contained the details of my experiences since he had visited me on Monday last and I asked him why he wanted to see them, adding that I was quite sure he was well aware of what I had been doing.

He replied: 'Yes, I have kept in touch with you for I have been given permission to link up with you mentally during the period in which I am responsible for your tuition. After that the link between your mental body and mine will immediately be broken, for we are not allowed to look into other people's minds, except in very special circumstances, similar to those which have applied to our association during the past two weeks. Every man is responsible to himself and to his Creator for what he does, and as you know, he is rewarded or has to suffer in accordance with the thoughts expressed and the deeds enacted. I asked to read through your notes because I want to know how much you remember of what you have done – without reading your record, I do not know that.'

He carefully read through to the end and continued: 'Your report concerning Tuesday night is quite good, for you remembered most of what took place during your visit to the Golden City. You missed out one rather important matter however for you have not mentioned that your guide took you to the outskirts of the city and pointed out to you a gathering that was listening to the thought-form they had created, representing Christ speaking to them. Both you and Daphne listened for a short time to what was said. You remarked to your guide that all that Christ was saying had already been recorded in the different gospels of the New Testament. That in itself should have been sufficient proof to you that it was not the great Being, who was known on earth as Christ, who was speaking, but merely the expression of that founder of the Christian faith that was part of the thoughts and minds of His most faithful followers. I am sure that had Christ himself been speaking – and He does still live and is still in control of the spiritual development of this planet – the impression of what he said would not so easily have been erased from your memory. Ask Daphne about the incident, when next you see her. She will certainly have remembered it.

'I am pleased with your description of Wednesday night's experiment, for it is better than I expected. I warned you of the difficulties you would experience in finding words to express mental activities, but I think that all who read your records will understand a little of what you have tried to describe. I am certainly satisfied that you have grasped most of what I tried to tell you in my last talk.

'Your peregrinations of last night need little comment from me. They have their value though, for you now understand that you have to consider the outlook of other people and to a great extent fit in with them, in the astral as on the physical plane. I am quite sure that your protegée Mary will be calling for you again in the very near future, and I know that you will endeavour to assist her with the many problems which she will have to face. It will be excellent experience for you.

'Today, in my last talk, I shall first tell you about "the third death" and what happens to the ego after he has dropped his remaining vehicle of consciousness, which we call the mental body, and lives for a period clothed in the only permanent vehicle he possesses – the *causal body*. I want you to listen very carefully to this, for many students seem to find it difficult to appreciate this information.

'The third death is very similar to the passing from the astral to the mental world, for the man just gradually loses consciousness and, having slipped out of the mental body, finds that he is in his causal body. The causal body is so called because it only functions on what is called the causal level, formed by the sixth and seventh spheres of the mental world. It is known as man's *permanent* vehicle because he has had it since he individualized out of the animal kingdom and became a separate human entity.

'The causal level is the natural home of the ego, and here he remains during the periods which we call incarnations when *part of himself is manifesting* at lower levels of consciousness and gaining the experiences necessary to free the ego from having to be reborn again and again in different physical bodies.

'The causal body changes every life merely by the addition to it of the experience the man has accumulated during his last incarnation: for this reason we sometimes refer to it as the *reservoir of knowledge*. An evolved man can tap this reservoir at will and draw down to the physical level the experiences of his past lives: this enables him to avoid having to learn certain things every time he has a new physical brain, for, in itself, the brain has no memory of past experiences. For this reason an evolved man has a great advantage over his less evolved brother – but each of us will be in the same position when we reach these stages of development. The most important lesson for us to learn is that it is only through our own efforts that progress can be made.

'More attention would be given to these matters were they better understood and more generally taught by those people who profess to be helpers of mankind. Few of us are able to conceive the fact that the *personality* discernible at physical level is but *a tiny part of the real man* – the ego – yet this ego, or *individuality*, overshadows and guides that personality to the best of his ability, within the limits allowed by the free will which is granted to all men when they have reached the standard of the human entity.

'At the causal level past, present and future are in reality one. Let me give you a physical plane example to illustrate this. Imagine for a moment a river, that twists and turns every few hundred yards. A man stationed on the deck of a river steamer, puffing its way on the journey it must accomplish, can see only that stretch of river in which the steamer is sailing at the moment. The stretch that exists beyond the bend to its rear, which it has already traversed, is unseen by him, and likewise, the course of the river beyond the curve to which the steamer is now being guided is also unseen. Let us suppose that another man is taking the same route in a helicopter; he would see the whole course of the river in one long sweep, the parts at the rear of the steamer and the parts well ahead of its present position being equally clear to his vision. To this man the scenery that the steamer has passed is just as visible as the scenery which meets the eyes of the passengers at the present moment, or that such people will see in the near future. To him there is no past and no future; all is indeed the present. The unevolved and the evolved man resemble the passenger on the steamer as compared to the one on the helicopter.

'At the causal level the ego is shown a full record of his past life in a series of pictures, rather as episodes on a filmstrip projector. These pictures show him exactly where he failed in his past life and where he excelled. They also show what his next life is *intended* to do for him and what changes in his character must be achieved before further progress can be made. The unevolved man sees all this, but owing to his limited intelligence does not grasp its significance in the way it is understood by the intellectual person. He is like the steamer passenger. On the other hand the evolved man, like the man travelling in the helicopter, sees immediately *why* he made the mistakes in his past life and not only the results of these errors. He determines that he will not fail in the same way in his next life. So the lessons he learnt from these pictures of the past life are built into the structure of his permanent atom – that reservoir of knowledge which contains the essence of his experiences in all his past lives – and when the time comes, in a future life, for him to make decisions on similar problems, the voice of conscience, which *is* the warning sent to him by the ego speaking from the plane on which his reservoir of knowledge exists, ensures that similar mistakes are not made a second time. He realizes why it is desirable for him to be born next time into a particular group of people or nation, because through such a birth he can obtain the environment that he needs; for this reason there is never any lack of co-operation on his part, when he is shown his future life. He knows only too well that the life arranged for him is the one which is best suited to ensure his greatest progress. To attain this in the shortest possible time is what every ego desires.

'Although we all enjoy our time lived at the egoic level, we have to leave it again in obedience to the law of evolution. We all want to leave when our time comes, for we feel within us the desire for further expression and experience; we know that progress in our evolution can only be achieved through countless lives, lived in the physical world. We realize that we cannot respond fully to the vibrations ruling at the causal level, until we have evolved to a stage where it is no longer necessary for us to be re-born again. That time comes when we have learnt all the lessons which life at the physical level can teach us and then our attention is drawn to other spheres of activity, far beyond the physical or astral levels. Egos who have reached this stage of perfect manhood sometimes decide, of their own volition, to remain in touch with the lower planes of consciousness, merely because of their great love of the human race and their desire to help mankind in its evolution. It is well that there are such great souls, for otherwise the progress of humanity would be much slower than it is at present.

'My description of the method of descent into rebirth should now not be difficult for you to understand, if you remember my previous analogy. The naked ego must clothe himself once again – in other words obtain three new bodies through which he can function on the planes of consciousness applicable to them. The first body he must obtain is made of mental matter (his underclothes) and to achieve this he turns his attention to his permanent atom in which, as you will remember, he has retained molecules corresponding to all the spheres which exist at the mental level. Taking the mental atom, he vivifies it and begins to draw around it other mental atoms from the matter which exists at the mental level, in the same way that a crystal, dropped into a solution, will cause other crystals to form round it. The matter that is drawn round him takes the form of his last mental body – the one he dropped at the end of his sojourn at the mental level – with one small difference; it is a better mental vehicle of consciousness than the last one, because it includes in it the result of his mental efforts in his past incarnation. He returns to this new life with a mental body that contains all the knowledge which he has built up in all his past lives, but still has no knowledge at all concerning the subjects he has so far neglected to study. This shows why some men in the world differ so greatly from others; their intellects are different because they possess different grades of mental bodies. Therefore a man who is the possessor of a fine intellect, acquired through experiences in many lives, should never take advantage of one who has less experience than himself – his task is to help not to hinder all his younger brothers.

'After creating for himself a new mental body, he goes a step further. He turns his attention to the astral atom and vivifies that. It at once gathers round itself other astral matter of exactly the same kind that he had in his last astral body, at the time when he dropped it. This means that all the emotional progress he made in his last life is included in the new astral body (his suit of clothes) which will serve him for this new existence. This new body contains within it the results of the work he did during the years he lived under astral plane conditions; for example if he had studied music deeply he will have an urge, in his next physical life, to take up music either as a profession or as a relaxation, and the development of musical talent will be very easy for him. The new astral body is much more sensitive than the old one, that is to say, it is able to register emotions more strongly than its predecessor.

'He must next have a physical body (his overcoat). This is acquired through the medium of being born in the normal way into a family in the world. The body is not necessarily a better type than that of the previous incarnation – much depends on the lessons which have to be learned in the new life, and the body given is the one needed at the moment. The first decision to be made is what changes in the character have to be accomplished. The answer to this decides various matters, the first of which is into which nation an ego will be born – for every nation has outstanding qualities. As you are British, I shall take your nation as an example of this. Devotion to duty is perhaps the most outstanding quality of the British character. If the ego coming into incarnation has, in his previous lives, refused to face up to difficulties – he might even have been so cowardly as to have committed suicide in one of his former lives – he obviously lacks the qualities that are so strongly a part of the British nation, so a life as a member of that group of families would undoubtedly build into the character of that individual what he needs at the moment, and at the end of that life his character will have altered considerably. When the nation into which the ego is to be born has been decided upon, it becomes necessary for a suitable family in that nation to be chosen – this is an intricate matter demanding much attention to detail and is one which is never left to chance. Although there might be dozens of families which could give him the environment he needs, it might be impossible for him to be considered for many of these because his actions in the past may have been such that he has not deserved the privilege of being born into such desirable circumstances. A family must be chosen through which he will come into contact with some of the personal links he has made in the past. Links are made through love, hate, marriage, parentage, being the father of an illegitimate child, deserting a woman in trouble and so on, and any karma made in these ways must be worked out. The question of heredity is another decision which has to be made and consideration is given as to whether the ego deserves health or must suffer from diseases; whether he is to be plain or handsome; the type of brain he deserves. The personal suitability of the parents receives consideration, the type of parents and the suitability of their marriage partnerships; whether the ego is to be born to a mother who *wants* a child and will therefore do all in her power to give him a suitable start in life; to parents who will treat him as a separate ego, considering his aptitudes when a child such as can be revealed by an urge to study music – which he may have acquired during his late astral visit – or to those who will frustrate him by paying no attention to such urges and interfere with his movements even when he is grown up; to people who will show tolerance in regard to religion or to those who will not.

'These arrangements having been made and a suitable astrological moment chosen, the child is born. It is now the task of the ego to overcome any obstacles of birth and environment with which he has been faced; sometimes men who have ultimately been leaders of nations have been born into poor and frustrating homes. The man who succeeds in overcoming the obstacles put in his path will make certain of associating with a family of high principles in desirable circumstances when his case is again considered for a further life in the physical world.

'Before concluding I must just touch on the vital subject of child upbringing. From what I have told you, you can realize that an ego can be much helped or hindered in his evolution by the attitude which his parents adopt to this subject. There are relatively so few people who have focused their attention upon the needs of children that it is now becoming difficult to find families suitable for the task of guiding advanced egos in their journeys.

'In order that you may realize the extreme importance of the upbringing of children, I shall first mention a few of the salient facts concerning human development.

'The development of man is divided into seven year periods, each marked by the appearance of a new power or quality. These steps are intimately associated with the developmental activities of the ductless glands in the physical body. What is termed "birth" is indeed only the birth of the visible physical body which comes to its high state of efficiency in a shorter time than do the invisible bodies of the ego. The physical foetus is enclosed in the protecting womb of the mother during gestation; in like manner the subtle vehicles – the etheric, astral and mental bodies of which I have endeavoured to give you some small degree of understanding in these talks – are enclosed in protecting envelopes of ether, desire stuff and mind stuff within the womb of the Universe, or Nature, until such time as they are sufficiently mature to withstand the conditions of the world. Physical development in the womb cannot be hastened so, in like manner, no attempt should be made to hasten the development of the non-physical bodies whilst still protected in the womb of Nature – this must just be allowed to proceed, under suitable child guidance. Therefore parents must be prepared to be guides, counsellors and friends of their children till they reach the age of twenty-one years, at which time their mental bodies are in the condition to take over, then, in order that the child may become a self-confident adult, *all parental control must cease*. Thereafter a parent should only proffer advice if this is asked for, on account of his greater experiences. To keep an adult attached to parental "apron strings" as is frequently done on one pretext or another by selfish parents is damaging to both child and parent.

'The first three septennial periods of man's development are marked by the birth, or coming to completion, of the etheric body at the stage of seven years, the time of the second dentition, the astral or desire body at fourteen years, the time of puberty, whilst the mental body which completes the man does not come into full activity till the age of twenty-one. In the new born child only the negative qualities of these bodies are active and, before it can make full use of its different vehicles, the positive qualities of each must be ripened. During the first seven years of life the forces operating along the negative pole of the ether are active, thus children of this age have clairvoyance of the same negative character as mediums; this is the reason why it is quite normal for young children to have play-mates invisible to grown-ups. Later, in the same way, the forces working in the desire body give only a passive capacity for feeling until the positive qualities develop; although emotions are freely displayed at this time, they are of a fleeting quality, never lasting. The years between fourteen and twenty-one, when the desire nature is boisterous and uncontrolled, are perhaps the most difficult years for

parents to deal with, for they must learn to practise the utmost tolerance and understanding at this time. Children are extremely sensitive to the forces working along the negative pole of the mind; this is
the reason why they are so extremely imitative and teachable and
must be understandably dealt with till the positive qualities take
over. As soon as this happens the ego is ready and eager to stand
alone, and must be allowed to do so. He will make mistakes, we have
all done so, it is one of the most important ways in which we learn
our lessons.

'In the early days of man's appearance on earth he received little
assistance from his parents who themselves had insufficient experience in evolution to give help to others, but in these later days conditions are so different that parentcraft should be regarded as a science
which it is necessary for all to study. The parents who practise
planned parenthood and have only two or three children to care for,
who have the necessary time to study and are prepared to do so are
able to equip themselves with the knowledge through which they
can become suitable guides for children. Parents must realize that
children are not playthings given to them to do with what they will,
but that they are fellow beings who have been entrusted to their care
and guidance by the Powers-that-Be. The suitability of the guidance
given to these fellow beings is one of the most important tasks
humanity is given to perform; under the law of karma parents will
be held responsible for the manner in which they carry out this work
and their own journey along the evolutionary path will be hastened
or retarded accordingly.

'All normal girls look forward to marriage, having a home of their
own and children; this is good, because it is of primary importance
that a small child should be reared in a household where it is loved
and *wanted*. To be successful and efficient wives however girls
should, *before marriage*, give attention to such subjects as household
management and domestic routine; the spending of money so as to
get the best value for it; the selection, preparation and cooking of
nutritious foodstuffs; they should understand the importance of
sufficient rest and sleep; the benefits to be derived from fresh air and

sunlight and the importance of both physical and mental culture. But in order to be successful mothers, they require to study still more deeply for they should begin to delve into some of the mysteries of Nature. In this study they should not be alone, for family responsibilities should be shared equally between fathers and mothers. Each has a part to play and a contribution to make in the upbringing of children. Wise parent-craft can only be practised by parents who have made at least some study of human development and who are willing to make some personal sacrifices. Adequately to perform the tasks allotted to them parents must be prepared to teach *by their own example* because there is nothing in the world so imitative as a child – in fact imitation is its main method of growth – so they must train themselves never to do anything they would be unwilling to see copied.

'In the guiding of the emotional development of a child there are two subjects which should be freely discussed in the home from the child's earliest years – one is sex and the other is religion. In their preparation for parenthood parents will have studied biology as affecting the plant, animal and human kingdoms hence should have no difficulty in telling quite small children the principles of reproduction in the different kingdoms, as suited to their years and understanding. For the very young they can make up fascinating fairy stories dealing with the plant kingdom. They can show the child the pistillate flowers, which they will liken to girls, and the staminate flowers, which they will liken to boys, they can show them the pollen in the anthers of the flowers and the pollen baskets on the legs of the bees.

'In the same way religion can be dealt with in an ordinary manner. No child can be expected to understand the doctrines and dogmas of the different religions; the consideration of that can wait till he has reached the age of thinking for himself. Religious instruction applicable to the age we are living in, and the one soon to come, is to be found in the life and teachings of Christ during His earthly sojourn in the body of Jesus, in that of the Lord Buddha and the other Founders of Religions. If we all knew and appreciated nothing else, we should have splendid patterns to live up to. Therefore let the teaching of religion to the young be that of the great dramas of the lives of these Teachers – lives which were sublime lessons of the possibilities of man. As with sex instruction this must be presented in a form suitable to the stage of understanding of the child – from a Bible, from stories written in more simple language and above all from parental example. If parents know and put into practise the Sermon on the Mount their children will exhibit those "patterns of reaction to life" which will serve them as a solid foundation of the understanding of Universal Love and Universal Brotherhood.

'The parents who have acquired tolerance and understanding through schooling themselves to see through the eyes of their children, approach things from their standpoint, touch with their fingers, question with their minds will, when their task of child education is finished, be in the very best position for getting to know themselves and for helping their fellow men tolerantly and wisely, which should be their task at this period of their own development – a task which can in its turn bring into being the positive qualities of their own spiritual make-up.

'I have been able to give you only a very brief outline of the importance of parental guidance and example in child education – in the time at my disposal I am unable to go more deeply into the question of methods for such education. All I can do is to point out that the need for this has at no time been greater or more urgent than it is in the world today. If parents continue to shirk their responsibilities, if they are unwilling to sacrifice their "pleasures" in order to take up the task of parentcraft, and if there continue to be as many broken homes as there now are, in which the love and understanding necessary for this task are no longer present, then consideration will have to be given to the question of whether upbringing of children – in age groups – in institutions by trained and understanding people might perhaps be the wisest solution of the problem. It would seem as if this is at least a field of enquiry which will have to be explored. Naturally there are arguments which can be brought forward in defence of both systems, but if the considered decision is in favour of home training, then some steps must surely be taken towards fostering wise and instructed parentcraft.

'I am satisfied that you know that we are not in the world by accident. You have realized that countless lives at the physical level are necessary if we are to gain sufficient experience to free us from the necessity of continuous births and deaths. You have proved for yourself that death, which is feared by so many people in the world, is a mere passing from one state of consciousness to another and that this passing should never be dreaded by anyone, even though it is sometimes preceded by a certain amount of physical pain. You are aware that the inequalities of life are not caused through a Divine Creator favouring some and not others, but that these inequalities are due to the different stages at which men stand at the moment on their journey towards perfection, or are produced by unwise actions on the part of such individuals in their past lives. I am sure you now realize that no work you do at this level is ever wasted, for at the end of each incarnation you carry your sheaves with you, to become part of the permanent atom, which is your reservoir of knowledge.

'After I leave you today, you will once more be the sole arbiter of your destiny. I hope that you will continue to follow up the link that has been re-made between you and Daphne, for you can help her in many things and she can help you. You are both destined to work together in a future life and the more you come to understand each other now, the more progress will be made when the time comes for you to live your lives together under physical plane conditions. It is just possible that before you pass over to the next world you may come across some one living at this level to whom you may feel attracted, and whom you may even want to marry. If this does happen, explain to Daphne what you contemplate doing, for deception has its repercussions, even in a case where one person is living in the astral world and the other in the physical world. Deception is always unwise, for it creates difficulties, which may take lives to eradicate completely.

'I do not think you will find that Charles will trouble you much more. As you happen to be an older ego than he is, it would be difficult for him to follow you along the road that you imagine to be the most suitable for him, but you can still help him and you will probably link up with him in a future life, as love creates a very strong link. Do not forget the responsibilities you have taken upon yourself with Mary, for although I do not think that they will be in any way arduous, yet they must not be neglected, for you accepted the opportunity. The astral helper whom you call Jim can be of great use to you and you to him, so cultivate his friendship whenever the opportunity offers. Remember that the knowledge which has been given to you, has not been given for your use solely. You have a responsibility to others less fortunate than yourself and I sincerely trust that you will never forget this. All true knowledge should be shared, not kept for the special benefit of the possessor, and I can assure you that you will not only be the happier for sharing your knowledge with others, but they also, will benefit from your assistance. You may find that many to whom you offer this bread of knowledge do not wish to eat it. Such people are not yet ready for the knowledge you offer, but that should not stop you from giving them the opportunity of listening to what you have to say.

'It is now time for me to bid you farewell. This does not mean that we shall never meet again, for the link that has been made between us during these last weeks will have its inevitable result. A link once made is seldom entirely broken. After I leave you I shall no longer know what you are doing, as I have been permitted to know during this short period in order to help me with your tuition, but I have no doubt that the progress you have made will be maintained. If, in the future, you find that you need me at any time, make a very strong thought-form to represent me and send out your desire for contact into the surrounding ether. I may not be in a position to answer your call immediately, but you may be very sure that I have received it, and I shall contact you as soon as the work I have on hand permit me to do so. I have greatly appreciated the understanding you have displayed on the occasions when my words might have appeared to criticize you and others in the world. Believe me, that was not my intention.

'One of the great philosophers once said: "Whenever the pupil is ready, the Master is always there." That is very true for, whatever your difficulties, you never stand entirely alone. They do not desert those who work on their behalf. Your efforts have brought you into touch with some of the great beings who endeavour to guide our footsteps along the paths most suitable for our progress. Your reaction to their help has made it possible for you to be brought into closer contact with them. They know our limitations and our difficulties. They only wait our desire to permit their help, for that assistance to be at once at our disposal.

'May the Peace which they so patiently work for, be with you and all who seek to lighten the burden of mankind. Farewell, until in God's good time we meet again.'